GEOLOGIC
EVOLUTION OF EUROPE

BY

ROLAND BRINKMANN

TRANSLATED FROM THE GERMAN

BY

JOHN E. SANDERS

WITH 46 FIGURES, 19 PLATES
AND 18 CORRELATION CHARTS

1·9·6·0

FERDINAND ENKE VERLAG STUTTGART
HAFNER PUBLISHING COMPANY NEW YORK

The Hafner Publishing Company is the exclusive distributor
for the USA and Canada

Translator's Preface

This book is a condensed version of the second volume of the 8th edition of the *Abriß der Geologie*, by Professor Roland Brinkmann, Bonn, Germany. The Abriss, a two-volume work covering both physical and historical geology, has become a more or less standard textbook for European geology students. Only those parts that deal with Europe have been included here to make an introduction to the geology of the area for English-speaking geologists. It is hoped that the book will prove a valuable traveling companion.

It has been a pleasure to become closely associated with Professor Brinkmann again and to repay in some measure his cordiality to my wife and me during visits to Bonn in 1954, when I was a National Research Council Post-Doctoral Fellow traveling in Europe.

I have made every effort to render a faithful replica of the book in English. Some changes have been required, of course, owing to the different stratigraphic terminology used in Europe and North America. I have added a few remarks concerning Sedgwick and Murchison's work in the southwest of England which led to the founding of the Devonian System, on Lyell's subdivisions of the Tertiary, and on Ewing and Donn's theory of the origin of Pleistocene climatic variations.

Readers will find this a product of the classical European school of tectonic philosophy. Much material presented may support the theories of the Kuenen school of sedimentology, but considerations of space made it impossible to go into details. On the other hand, the concept of *Schwellen* (ridge) and *Becken* (basin) facies controlled by folds growing beneath the sea during sedimentation, long a fixture of European geology, has attracted the attention of American geologists only rather recently. This concept, based on the known effects on marine sedimentation exerted by bottom topography, is supported by the classical examples of the Devonian of the Rhenish Schiefergebirge and the Mesozoic of the Alps.

John E. Sanders

New Haven, Connecticut, 17 December 1959

Contents

Explanation of the Correlation Charts

Marine facies or beds with marine ingressions

Brackish and continental facies

▲ Glacial facies

Breaks in the sequence

Significant transgression

Large or small coal content

Intense or weak volcanic activity

Intense orogenic phase with intrusion of plutonic rocks

Weaker orogenic phase

Dol.	Dolomite
Grauw.	Graywacke
K.	Limestone
Kongl.	Conglomerate
Schf.	Shale
Sdst.	Sandstone
lst.	Limestone
sl.	Slate

No facies are distinguished on the table of the Archean and Algonkian.

The thickness figures in general refer to average values, whereas maximum values are designated as "—..m".

Schichten, Sch., -sch.	Beds, strata
Abteilung	Subdivision
Stufe	Stage
Gruppe, -gr.	Group
Hangendes	Overlying beds
Liegendes	Underlying beds
Leitfossilien	Index fossils
Oberer	Upper
Mittlerer	Middle
Unterer	Lower

Chapter 1.

History of European Geology

Geology as a science was born in Europe. This is true in three respects. During the course of history on this continent and in the lands adjoining the Mediterranean Sea the higher forms of civilization first originated and laid the foundation for scientific progress. The evolution of science, to be sure, followed its own individual laws, but it was influenced and shaped simultaneously by human and geological factors. Geology, in its beginnings a purely descriptive natural science, derived its main impetus firstly from the intellectual climate of the time, secondly from the personalities of its founders, and thirdly from the peculiarity of Europe's geological structure.

The origins of geology date back to classical times, and at the beginning of the modern age it was considerably developed by the discoveries of L. da Vinci, G. Agricola and N. Steno. But as an independent science it was founded scarcely 200 years ago by the Scot, J. Hutton, and the German, A. G. Werner.

Proceeding from the Calvinistic philosophy of predestination Hutton believed that God created the world in pre-history, but since then has surrendered His control to Natural Law. For Hutton it was the essential task of geology to grasp by observation the principles of Natural Law. Present events, therefore, became for him the key to the geologic past. The almost imperceptible slowness with which the modern changes of the Earth proceed opened to Hutton a vision of the immeasurable length of geologic time. He recognized also that currents of water were not the only agent to shape the surface of the Earth; but on the contrary that the most important forces came from within. He thereby acknowledged the tectonic structure of the Earth's crust as a separate subject for study.

Werner's outlook was founded on an entirely different philosophical basis. He was convinced that the creation of the world was contained in Earth history. His theory of the origin of the Earth was, after all, only another creation story put into scientific terms. Werner thought that a hot primeval ocean had existed in the beginning and from it the rocks had crystallized in a definite order, beginning with granite. Werner attributed

1 Brinkmann, Geologic Evolution of Europe

little significance to the inner forces of the Earth. This is revealed by his explanation of volcanism, which he regarded as a purely surface phenomenon fed by seams of burning coal. It remains to Werner's credit, however, that he founded for geology (as the Swiss naturalist, H. B. de Saussure, named the young science) a system of names for rocks, minerals and structures, which is still used.

At the beginning of the 19th century a new generation replaced the "heroic age" of Hutton and Werner. W. Smith (1761—1839) recognized that the petrified remains of organisms occur in the ground always in the

Fig. 1. James Hutton
1726—1797

Fig. 2. Abraham Gottlob
Werner 1749—1817

same regular succession. Fossils were thereby raised from the status of mere curiosities. G. Cuvier (1769—1832) first learned to demonstrate this by means of comparative anatomical considerations. Ch. Lyell (1797—1875) took up the ideas of Hutton and in his textbook (1830) sought to prove the similarity of geological processes throughout the entire history of the Earth. L. von Buch (1774—1852) traversed almost all the lands of Europe as a traveler and keen observer ("Mente et Malleo") and was the undisputed expert of his time.

By the middle of the century the superstructure of the science was being erected on this foundation. Geology entered an epoch of individual investigations, of geologic map-making, classification of fossilized fauna and flora, and the increasingly exact elucidation of Earth history. This development was materially assisted by the foundation of governmental geological surveys, geological societies and of separate professorships in the universities. The Geological Survey of Great Britain originated in the year 1835; the Austrian governmental geological establishment, in 1849. The oldest geological societies are the English (1807), the French (1830), and the German (1848). The example of Freiberg in Saxony, where Werner occupied the first Chair of Geology in the world, was followed by almost all universities on the Continent in the course of time.

We are indebted to a large number of geologists for important advances. There were Th. Kjerulf, W. C. Brögger, and V. M. Goldschmidt in Norway; A. E. Törnebohm, and O. Torell in Sweden; J. J. Sederholm, and P. Eskola in Finland; H. de la Beche, R. I. Murchison, W. Buckland, and A. Geikie in the British Isles. From central Europe the Belgians, J. F. Omalius d'Halloy, and A. Dumont; the Germans A. Goldfuss, F. A. Quenstedt, E. Beyrich, K. Zittel, H. Stille, and H. Cloos; the French E. de Beaumont, A. Brongniart, M. Bertrand, Ch. Barrois, P. Termier, and E. Haug should be mentioned. The study of the Alps was divided between the Swiss geologists, H. B. de Saussure, A. Escher, J. Thurmann, A. Heim, and E. Argand, and the Austrians F. v. Hauer, M. Neumayr, and E. Suess. Fr. Schmidt, A. Karpinsky, and A. Tschernitschew worked in European Russia; W. Brocchi, in Italy; and A. Boué and A. Philippson, in the Balkans.

Supplementary articles

F. D. Adams: The Birth and Development of the Geological Sciences. New York 1954.
G. Agricola: Ausgewählte Werke. Herausgeg. von H. Prescher. Berlin since 1955.
G. Agricola: Gedenkschrift, herausgeg. v. d. Deutsch. Akad. d. Wiss., Berlin 1955.
E. Bailey: Geological Survey of Great Britain. London 1952.
M. Brockmann-Jerosch u. a.: Albert Heim. Basel 1952.
S. v. Bubnoff: Grundprobleme der Geologie. Berlin 1954.
H. Cloos: Conservation with the Earth. New York 1953.
A. Geikie: The Founders of Geology. London 1905.
M. Semper: Die geologischen Studien Goethes. Leipzig 1914.
K. A. v. Zittel: Geschichte der Geologie und Paläontologie. München and Leipzig 1899.

Important textbooks, manuals and periodicals
Europe:

S. v. Bubnoff: Geologie von Europa. Berlin 1926.
H. Stille: Die assyntische Tektonik im geologischen Erdbild. Beih. Geol. Jb. 22. Hannover 1958.
H. Stille: Das mitteleuropäische variszische Grundgebirge im Bilde des gesamteuropäischen. Beih. Geol. Jb. 2. Hannover 1951.

Northern Europe:

O. Holtedahl: Norges Geologi. Norges Geol. Undersök. 164. Oslo 1953.
N. H. Magnusson u. a.: Sveriges Geologi. Stockholm 1957.
V. Madsen u. a.: Übersicht über die Geologie von Dänemark. Danmarks geol. Undersög. V, 4. Kopenhagen 1928.
Norsk Geologisk Tidskrift. Since 1905.
Geologiska Föreningens Förhandlingar. Since 1874.
Meddelelser fra Dansk Geologisk Forening. Since 1894.

Central Europe:

R. Brinkmann: Abriß der Geologie. Stuttgart 1959.
S. v. Bubnoff: Einführung in die Erdgeschichte. Berlin 1956.
E. Kayser: Lehrbuch der Geologie. Stuttgart 1924.
P. Dorn: Geologie von Mitteleuropa. Stuttgart 1960.
P. Fourmairier: Prodrome d'une Description géologique de la Belgique. Liège 1954.
A. J. Pannekoek: Geological History of the Netherlands. 's-Gravenhage 1956.
Neues Jahrbuch für Mineralogie, Geologie und Paläontologie. Since 1807.
Zeitschrift der Deutschen Geologischen Gesellschaft. Since 1849.
Geologische Rundschau. Since 1910.
Geologie & Mijnbouw. Since 1921.
Annales de la Societé géologique de Belgique. Since 1874.
Bulletin de la Société Belge de Géologie. Since 1887.

Alpine region:

J. Cadisch: Geologie der Schweizer Alpen. Basel 1953.
F. X. Schaffer: Geologie von Österreich. Vienna 1951.
Eclogae geologicae Helvetiae. Since 1888.
Mitteilungen der Geologischen Gesellschaft in Wien. Since 1908.

Western Europe:

E. Haug: Traité de Géologie. Paris 1920.
M. Gignoux: Géologie stratigraphique. Paris 1950.
R. Abrard: Géologie de la France. Paris 1948.
J. W. Evans & C. J. Stubblefield: Handbook of the Geology of Great Britain. London 1929.
J. K. Charlesworth: The Geology of Ireland. London 1953.
L. J. Wills: A Palaeogeographical Atlas of the British Isles. London 1952.
Regional Geology of Great Britain. London since 1948.
Bulletin de la Société géologique de France. Since 1830.
Quarterly Journal of the Geological Society. Since 1833.
Geological Magazine. Since 1874.

Southern Europe:

Bolletino della Società Geologica Italiana. Since 1882.

Eastern Europe:

S. v. Bubnoff: Fennosarmatia. Berlin 1952.
N. S. Schatski & A. Bogdanow: Grundzüge des tektonischen Baues der Sowjetunion. Berlin 1958.
Geological structure of USSR (Russ.). Moscow 1958.
Soviet Geology (Russ.). Since 1933.

Chapter 2.

Precambrian

Preliminary Remarks

Historical geologic investigation began with quietly deposited and little altered sediments of the most recent past which abound with well-preserved fossils. Using these as a basis, it gradually became possible to understand more ancient periods of Earth history, but disturbances of strata, intense alteration of the rocks, and the rarity and obscure significance of the organic remains accordingly rendered knowledge more difficult to attain. Investigation of the groups of Precambrian formations has only in more recent years begun to make progress, but is today advancing fast.

Boundaries and classification. The techniques that have been especially developed for study of the Precambrian rocks are determined by the scarcity of fossils in the deposits, by association of the strata with eruptives, and by the degree of metamorphic transformations. The oldest series have been recrystallized and impregnated with material that was formerly molten. These are unconformably overlain by younger, less altered strata. The intrusions into the underlying rocks show a truncated, erosional contact with the rocks above. Basal conglomerates of the younger systems are composed of eroded blocks from the older systems. The practical use of these techniques, which here amounts to a subdivision according to great orogenetic-magmatic phases, has led to a classification of the Precambrian history of the Earth into two periods, an older Archean and younger Algonkian (= Proterozoic). More recently, age measurements by means of radioactive disintegration of U, K, and Rb have increased in significance; yet in Europe, particularly Central Europe, only a few figures are available.

Distribution. Archean and Algonkian rocks outcrop over large areas in the central zones of the folded mountain chains and in the primeval cratons, the continental cores that were rigidified in pre-Paleozoic time. The older rocks in the central zones have generally been folded repeatedly and retain the imprints of younger orogenies and intrusions so that it is difficult to distinguish what is original. The Precambrian rocks can be examined to greater advantage in the old massifs, which have been but little or entirely unaffected by later movements. Our knowledge depends chiefly on the investigations of the Baltic Shield (A. G. Högbom, J. J. Sederholm, P. Geijer, P. Eskola, N. H. Magnusson, A. Polkanov, and W. Timofeyev) and of the Ukrainian Massif (W. Laskarev and D. Sobolev).

Principal Regions (Figs. 3—8)

Sweden and Finland. In the Baltic Shield the geologic succession begins with the Supra-Crustal complex, which over great distances is composed of laminated fine-grained leptites and somewhat coarser-grained leptite-

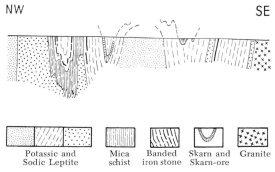

| Potassic and Sodic Leptite | Mica schist | Banded iron stone | Skarn and Skarn-ore | Granite |

Fig. 3. Structure section through the leptite formation of the Norberg iron-ore deposit (central Sweden).
Scale 1 : 35,000 (After P. Geijer)

Fig. 4. Archean migmatite with relict fabric after folded strata.
Pörtö, Finland (after C. E. Wegmann)

gneisses. Predominantly liparitic to andesitic effusives and tuffs of extreme Atlantic or Mediterranean chemical composition are concealed within this metamorphic guise, as can be recognized in less disturbed regions. Locally these are preserved almost unchanged as compact, brittle Hälleflint. In addition to Hälleflint, sandstone, graywacke and shale appear, but chiefly in the upper part of the series, and even deposits of sedimentary iron ore and limestone, with which ore deposits of metasomatic origin are often associated. It is these ore deposits, together with a series of great apatite-magnetite ore-bodies of magmatic origin, also intruded during the Archean, which make the iron fields of central Sweden and Lapland so rich (Fig. 3).

A large late-Archean mountain-building epoch created the Svekofennides, a fold chain with more or less northwest strike that crosses Sweden and southern Finland. At the same time magmatic masses were emplaced.

Fig. 5. The tectonic units of the Scandinavian-Finnish basement (after H. Backlund and others). Norw. u. Mar.=Norwegosamides and Marealbides, fold nuclei of perhaps pre-Svekofennidian age

The first, a generation of synkinematic granite (the so-called primeval granite), concordantly intruded the country rock. The second, late-kinematic, more discordant generation, caused the radical transformation of the basement, which may have proceeded to total melting (Fig. 4).

The Algonkian begins with coarse-grained, terrestrial waste products, conglomerates and arkoses, derived from the granites, leptites, and migmatites of the Svekofennidian Mountains. Later the basin of sedimentation sank below sea-level and was filled with thick deposits. Crossbedded quartzite with ripple-marks, graywackes, dolomite beds, and mainly uniform, thinly bedded flysch-like phyllites, alternate with predominantly basic lava flows. Deposits of graphitic schist signify organic life; in Finland even traces of bitumen occur (the so-called Schungite). The Karelian terminated with a considerable phase of folding and intrusion. This created the Gotokarelian Mountains, whose chains striking more or

W   E

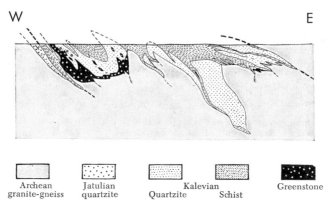

| Archean granite-gneiss | Jatulian quartzite | Kalevian Quartzite | Schist | Greenstone |

Fig. 6. Structure section through the Karelides, East Finland.
Scale 1 : 500,000 (after C. E. Wegmann)

less NW—SE wound around the older, rigid Svekofennidian Massifs (Fig. 5, 6).

The Gotokarelidian folding was the last great orogenesis of Alpine type on the Baltic Shield. The tectonic structure was solidified in the younger Algonkian. The establishment of the fracture- and fault networks, which thanks to the retouching by the ice of the Quaternary glaciers, are so clear on every map of the Baltic region, took place at this time. Moderately thick continental deposits replaced thick marine geosynclinal sediments. The core of the Baltic Shield was never again inundated by the sea after Karelian time; and even the marginal rims have, since then, been only sporadically subjected to shallow transgressions. The Jotnian consists of red sandstones and conglomerates. Mud cracks, ripple-marks (Fig. 7) and ventifacts bespeak a continental

Fig. 7. Jotnian sandstone with ripple marks and mud cracks. Sweden

origin under an arid climate. Magmatic activity came to a close in the Baltic Shield with the formation of the Rapikivi granite masses, which are widespread laccolithic plates intruded at shallow depths.

Eastern Europe, from the Urals to the Black Sea, consists of a crystalline base, the Russian platform, which like the Baltic Shield, comprised a part of the north-European primeval craton. The Precambrian basement is generally covered by flat-lying strata and comes to light only in Karelia, Kola, and the Ukraine.

In *Karelia* and *Kola*, the Archean and older Algonkian contains magnetite quartzite, as in Scandinavia. In the arrangement and properties of the rocks of the higher Algonkian there exists a close similarity with Finland.

The core of the *Ukrainian Massif* is composed of biotite-plagioclase gneiss of probable Archean age, which has been transected by syntectonic granite of the Kirovograd complex. Unconformably above this lie 2000—3000 m. of lower Algonkian diabase, tuffs, and shales with intercalations of iron-ore beds, which are mined at Krivoi Rog. As in the Baltic areas, red sandstone and conglomerate with porphyries were formed at the end of the Precambrian.

The remaining part of the Russian platform is composed of a similar succession of rocks. Drill cores and magnetic anomalies indicate that the Karelides continue from Finland with a more southerly strike via the high magnetic disturbance at Kursk to Krivoi Rog.

Norwegian Mountains and British Isles. Whereas the Baltic Shield rigidified in the course of the Precambrian, the crust along its northwest margin maintained mobility. The Caledonian geosyncline originated here at the conclusion of the Algonkian; it stretched from the British Isles via western Scandinavia to the Arctic. The basal part of the sediment content of the Caledonian geosyncline, ranging from the late Algonkian until the beginning of the Cambrian, is predominantly coarse-grained. This scarcely metamorphosed series nearly 1500 m. thick outcrops in southern Norway as Sparagmite. In the Scottish Highlands and in north Ireland it has been more intensely altered and is known as the Moine and Dalradian. As does the Dalradian, the Sparagmite contains a tillite bed; in Scandinavia the glaciers seem to have descended into the geosyncline from the East. In northwest Scotland and the Hebrides we enter upon the opposite shore of the Caledonian geosyncline; this forms a counterpart to the Baltic Shield. As in Sweden, variegated non-marine sandstones (Torridonian) here lie almost undisturbed on a highly cristalline plate of Lewisian gneiss.

Arctic. The Caledonian geosyncline continued from Norway toward the region of the North Pole. Here too its oldest filling is composed of late Algonkian strata, 3000—5000 m. thick. In northeast Spitzbergen they

are called the lower Hecla Hook, and in eastern Greenland the Greenlandian or Eleonore Bay series; they everywhere contain tillite.

Central Europe. Archean rocks of the Baltic Shield occur at depth under
the southern Baltic region and part of northern Germany, as wells on
the Danish islands and pebbles in the Carboniferous of the Lausitz indicate.
Further south one reaches a domain with thick Algonkian deposits. Today
they are more or less intensely metamorphosed, and have been transected
and partly melted by likewise gneissified silicic plutonic rocks. This
suggests that a great orogenesis took place in central Europe toward the
end of the Precambrian. But many of the crystalline schists of central
Europe may possibly be much younger, for in the Cambrian a new geosyncline (p. 17), which was the site of repeated mountain-building episodes
during the course of the Paleozoic, originated in the Algonkian zone of
subsidence.

Bohemia forms an excellent point of departure for this question. Near
Prague a thick sequence of coarse graywackes, shales, and graphitic
quartzites (meta-lydites) with intercalated diabase (spilite) lies unconformably below the Cambrian. The exact age is unknown. Metamorphism increases toward the S. The crystalline core of the Bohemian
Massif (the Moldanubian), consists in the Bavarian-Bohemian Forest, in
the Austrian Waldviertel, in Moravia and in Sudetia, for the most part
of graphite-bearing gneiss, marble, and quartzite. Below this series of
possible Algonkian age that is connected with amphibolites, lie katazonal
orthogneiss, migmatite, and granulite, which probably belong to the
Archean.

Central German Uplands. Again it is principally Algonkian that occurs
at or near the surface in the anticlinal cores of the Paleozoic folds
which surround the Bohemian Massif from the Fichtelgebirge through
Saxony almost as far as Silesia. We meet with it in faintly metamorphic
form in the southern Fichtelgebirge, in the Thuringian Schiefergebirge,
in the Lausitz, and in the Bober-Katzbach Range, where it is recognizable
by its characteristic graphitic quartzites and marbles. It outcrops more
intensely altered and in association with Early Paleozoic in Vorspessart, in
the northwestern Thuringian forest, in the Granulit- and Erzgebirge, in
the Iser- and Riesengebirge; and in western and eastern Sudetia.

The gneiss of the Erzgebirge forms several domes composed of recumbent folds. The Gray gneiss, whose sedimentary origin is shown by intercalations of metamorphosed conglomerate, after meso- to epizonal re-
crystallization in the youngest Algonkian or in the Cambro-Ordovician,
was intruded by alkalic granite, which today appears as Red gneiss. The
rocks of the Granulitgebirge are perhaps composed of similar material (Red
gneiss and metamorphosed Algonkian), only they have undergone still more

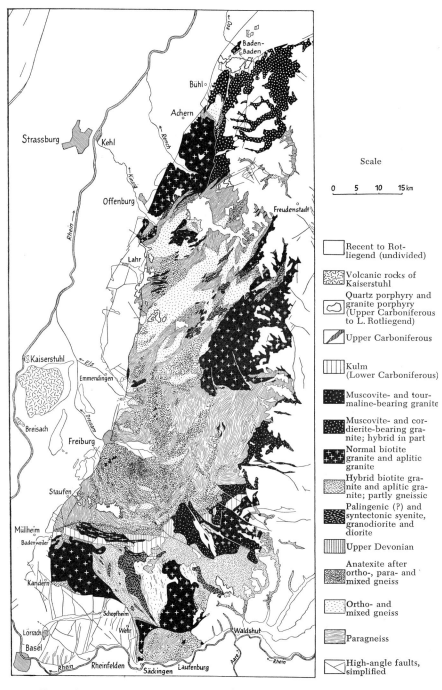

Scale

0   5   10   15 km

Recent to Rot-
liegend (undivided)

Volcanic rocks of
Kaiserstuhl

Quartz porphyry and
granite porphyry
(Upper Carboniferous
to L. Rotliegend)

Upper Carboniferous

Kulm
(Lower Carboniferous)

Muscovite- and tour-
maline-bearing granite

Muscovite- and cor-
dierite-bearing gra-
nite; hybrid in part

Normal biotite
granite and aplitic
granite

Hybrid biotite gra-
nite and aplitic gra-
nite; partly gneissic

Palingenic (?) and
syntectonic syenite,
granodiorite and
diorite

Upper Devonian

Anatexite after
ortho-, para- and
mixed gneiss

Ortho- and
mixed gneiss

Paragneiss

High-angle faults,
simplified

Fig. 8. The crystalline basement of the Black Forest (after D. Hoenes and K. R. Mehnert)

intense metamorphism. The basement of the Black Forest and Vosges is similar to that of the Erzgebirge in that it has resulted from a thick, uniform clastic sedimentary sequence. By intrusion of granitic melts and a double metatexis ortho- and paragneiss (Schapbach and Rench gneiss), originated interlocking in extensive mixed gneiss zones (Fig. 8).

In the *Ardennes*, the variegated phyllite and quartzite of Deville may possibly be assigned to the Precambrian.

The Alps consist of a backbone that is composed of metamorphic rocks, the central Alpine crystallines. If one attempts to remove the influence of the Alpine mountain-building, then there remains a core of meso- to katazonal gneisses, mica schists, amphibolites, and marbles, which have been invaded by old granites. In the Western Alps this sequence is older than the Upper Carboniferous; how far it extends backward is unknown. In the Eastern Alps the oldest known fossils go back to the Ordovician. Here, perhaps, one can infer that part of the so-called Old-Crystallines belong to the Precambrian.

General features

Climate and environment. While in the Precambrian the chemical precipitation and sedimentation processes were not fundamentally different from those of later times, so far as the facies of the sediments show; they did, however, deviate in many respects.

Worthy of note, particularly in the Archean, is the preponderance of incompletely sorted clastic deposits, such as graywacke and graywacke-shales. Better sorted quartzites and shales begin to appear in quantity for the first time in the later Precambrian. It is the same with the chemical sediments, limestones and dolomites. The laminated iron ores which are found throughout the world and may have originated in shallow seas by alternate deposition of hydrated iron and silica gel, have been formed under conditions which have not been experienced since. In part the peculiarity of the Precambrian sediments is explained by the fact that almost the only remains we have are of the quickly sedimented fillings of rapidly sinking basins; well-sorted deposits of epicontinental regions, on the other hand, are scarcely preserved. Furthermore, the predominance of mechanical deposition over precipitation, of physical over chemical rock decomposition, bespeaks a chiefly cool and humid climate — apart from the absence of a plant cover in the primitive deserts which were deprived of plants, that would have promoted the formation of clastics. On the basis of the red color of the sediment a change to semi-arid conditions only took place at the very end of the Algonkian.

Our idea that the Precambrian climate was not much different from today's is confirmed by evidence from glaciers. In the late Algonkian

Archäikum und Algonkium

Zeitalter	Zeit in Mill.J.	Baltisch - Russischer Schild					Kaledonische Geos.		Hebriden-Urkraton
		Schweden	Finnland	Karelien	Ukraine	Kola	Norwegen	Schottland	
Hangendes:	−500	Unterkambrium (Hardeberga - Sdst.)	(Waldai - Stufe)		(Wolhyn. St.)	Kambrium	Unt. Kambrium (Discinella - Sdst.)	Mittel-Kambrium	Unt. Kambrium (Basalqu.)
						Hyper-boräikum	Sparagmit	Dalradian	
Algonkium (Protero-zoikum)		Dala u. Dala-Sdst. / Almesåkra Dala-Porphyr	Jotnium / Jotnischer Sdst. / Hoglandium	Jotnium	Owrutsch, Polesje u. Serdowo	Jotnium	Trysil-Sdst.	Moinian	Torridonian
	−1500	Lina-u. Rätan-Granit / Dal u. Bälinge	Onas-Granit, Rapakivi	Sujsar / Segosero u. Onega		Petschenga	?		Laxfordian
			Kare-lium / Kumpu						
		Pajala, Åmål u. Vakko	Lapponium, Jatulium u. Kalevium	Ladoga, Gimol u. Parandowo	Dnjepr u. Kursk	Kejv u. Tundra			
	−1800	Stockholm - u. Revsundgran. Urgranit	Hangö- Granit / Gneisgranit		Kirowograd-Granit			Lewisian	
Archäikum		Skellefte u. Larsbo / Leptitserie	Bottnium / Svionium	Belomorje	Teterew u. Bug	Kola		Scourian	

glacial deposits are especially widespread. Their extent proves that they were deposited by continental ice, not by individual valley glaciers. One regards them correctly, therefore, as signs of an infra-Cambrian (or Varanger) ice age.

Crustal movements and magmatism. The formulation of the concepts Archean and Algonkian took place at the end of the last century, when it was supposed that the Precambrian formed a relatively short prelude to Earth-history, which began in the Cambrian. Proceeding from the notion that there were only few mountain-building episodes which anyway decreased in intensity, one simply assigned the intensely recrystallized rocks to the Archean, and the less altered rocks, to the Algonkian. Since then geological researches and absolute age measurements have shown that we had enormously underestimated the duration of Precambrian time. The old massifs have not been created in a few orogenic phases, but are composed of a large number of mountains of different ages. The results of Precambrian folding are the primeval cratons (Fig. 46), the rigid platforms of the Baltic Shield, Greenland, etc., which have remained stable up to the present day. Between them remained more mobile crustal areas, from which the geosynclines of the Paleozoic era arose as early as the younger Algonkian.

Retrospect. The Precambrian, even though it does not differ fundamentally from the younger periods, forms nevertheless a remarkable section of Earth history. Life was in its first stages of development. Dry land was uninhabited. The sea, too, can have been only very sparsely populated to judge by the scarcity of fossils in its deposits. The Algonkian sediments are still quite varied. But the more remote the time, the more restricted the choice is to a few kinds of clastics. At the same time the proportion of magmatic rocks increases; these may be lavas and tuff, or plutonic melts and solutions which invaded the basement. Even the ore deposits of the Precambrian are noteworthy for size and type. The sedimentary iron ores belong to a group which is unknown in later periods. The same is true of a number of important ore-bodies of liquid-magmatic and contact-pneumatolytic origin.

Supplementary articles

P. Eskola: Conditions during the earliest geological times: Ann. Ac. Sc. Fenn. A 36, 4. 1932.

P. Geijer and N. H. Magnusson: Mellansvenska Järnmalmernas Geologi. Sver. Geol. Unders. Ca 35. 1944.

K. Mehnert: Petrographie und Abfolge der Granitisation im Schwarzwalde: Abh. N. Jb. f. Min. 85 ff. Since 1953.

Chapter 3.

Cambrian

Preliminary Remarks

Boundaries and classification. After the essential outlines of the stratigraphic synthesis of the later formations had been elucidated, at the beginning of the 19th century attention was turned to the transition- or graywacke-terranes. A. Sedgwick (1836) was able to shed the first light on this previously undivided complex by postulating, after many years of research in the mountains of Wales, the erection of the Cambrian. At first this newly proposed theory remained disputed. Only with the discovery of the Cambrian fauna by R. I. Murchison (1839) did the position and subdivision of the system attain a solid footing. For its further development we are chiefly indebted to Ch. Lapworth in England, Th. Kjerulf and W. C. Brögger in Norway, N. Angelin, I. G. O. Linnarsson and G. Holm in Sweden, Fr. Schmidt in the eastern Baltic area, and J. Barrande in Bohemia.

The boundaries and subdivisions of the Cambrian are clearly defined. The underlying rocks consist mostly of non-fossiliferous Precambrian; moreover, the lower contact is almost always marked by a stratigraphic gap, often by an unconformity. The upper boundary is drawn at the sudden appearance of the rich Ordovician fauna.

Distribution. A new major cycle of Earth history began in the late Algonkian. The crust had resolved itself into cratons and geosynclines, a pattern which has lasted, until the present, which now, thanks to the better and more complete record of the strata, can be delimited more clearly than formerly. The cratonic massifs, such as the Baltic Shield (A. H. Westergård, A. Öpik, K. Grönwall, Ch. Poulsen and P. Thorslund), carry a thin covering of Cambrian sediments that today are still horizontal. In the geosynclines, in Wales (E. Cobbold), the mountains of Norway (J. Kiaer, Th. Vogt, and G. Henningsmoen) and in central Europe (R. Richter, M. Schwarzbach, R. Kettner, and J. Czarnocki), thicker units of later folded Cambrian strata were deposited.

Principal Regions (Fig. 9)

In the mountains of **Norway** and in the **British Isles,** the Caledonian geosyncline originated in the late Algonkian; it continued into the Arctic at one end, and into western Europe at the other. The northwest boundary consisted of the old gneiss massive of the Hebrides; it is covered by only a relatively thin, chiefly calcareous, Cambrian section (Fig. 11). The filling of the central part of the trough, which attains more than 5000 m., is revealed in the classical area of Wales. Toward the SE, approaching central England, the filling goes thinner again. Here we approach the other margin of the basin, which on the Scandinavian peninsula was formed by the Baltic Shield. Subsidence advanced especially unequally. The oldest marine fauna of the Lower Cambrian that is characterized by Holmia and Callavia has been identified only on the SE margin of the geosyncline (South Wales, Shropshire, north of Oslo). Only by the Middle Cambrian, from which fossils have been discovered on the west Norwegian coast, in North Wales, and in the upper part of the Scottish Dalradian, was the

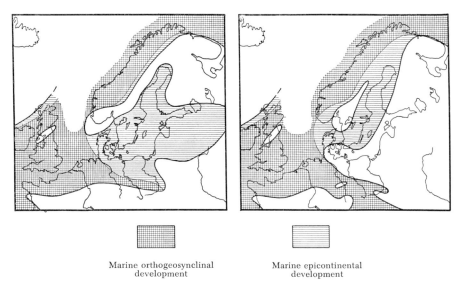

Marine orthogeosynclinal
development

Marine epicontinental
development

Fig. 9. Paleogeography of the Cambrian in northern Europe. Lower Cambrian (Holmia stage), on the left; beginning of the Middle Cambrian, on the right

flooding completed. At the same time the basin deepened, particularly in Wales. Here the thick, almost unfossiliferous, red and green coarse-grained deposits of the Harlech and Caerfai, whose base may extend back into the late Algonkian, are overlain by the dark shales of the Menevian. The micaceous sandstone of the Upper Cambrian Lingula flags originated as the sea got shallower.

Baltic Lands. After the crustal movements in the Baltic Shield had gradually ceased in the course of the Algonkian, the basement became truncated during the interval between the Jotnian and Cambrian by an almost table-like denudation surface, the sub-Cambrian peneplain. At the same time as the sea occupied the Caledonian geosyncline, it also spread over the adjoining shield. So developed a Cambrian forerunner of the present-day Baltic basin; but the deepest subsidence was shifted some-what toward the E, into the Baltic lands and the region around Lenin-

Plate 1. Cambrian index fossils

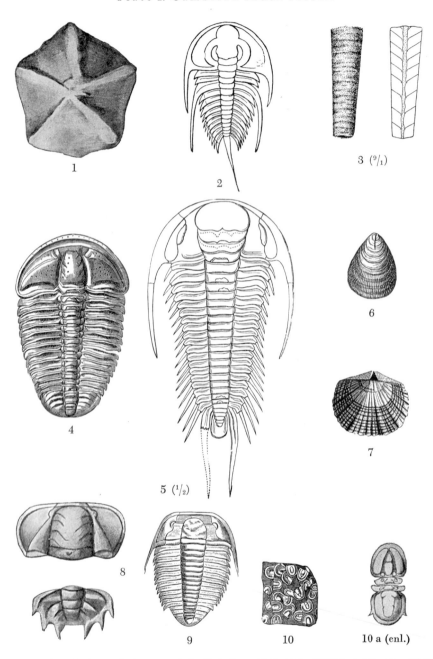

Lower Cambrian: 1. *Spatangopsis* (= *Medusites* aut.) *lindströmi* LINN. 2. *Olenellus gilberti* MEEK. 3. *Volborthella tenuis* FR. SCHMIDT. Middle Cambrian: 4. *Conocoryphe sulzeri* SCHLOTH. 5. *Paradoxides gracilis* BOECK. Upper Cambrian: 6. *Lingulella davisii* M'COY. 7. *Orusia lenticularis* WAHL. 8. *Peltura scarabaeoides* WAHL. 9. *Olenus truncatus* BRÜNN. 10, 10 a. *Agnostus pisiformis* L.

Kambrium

Abteilungen	Leit-fossilien	Baltisch – Russischer Schild						Hebriden-masse	Kaledon. Geosynkline		Mitteleuropäische Geosynkline			Mediterrane Geos.	Nord-amerika
		Zonenfolge	Russische Plattform	Estland	Bornholm	Schonen	Väster-götland	Nord-schottland	Wales	Norweg. Hochgeb.	Lausitz u. Bober-Katzbachgeb.	Böhmen		Marokko	
Hangendes:	Dictyonema		Devon (old Red)	(Obolensdst.) *Ordovizium* (Dictyonemaschiefer)				Ordovizium (Durnesskalk z.T.)	Ordovizium (Tremadoc)	↑	*Ordovizium* dα (Krušnáhora-Sch.)		Obolensdst.	Ordovizium (Arenig)	Ordovician
Ober-kambrium	Olenus	Acerocare							1000 m						Trempealeauan
		Peltura			20 m	50 m	15 m		Dolgelly		1000 m	700 m Sch. v. Ohrazenice (Porphyrit. Tuffe Konglomerate)	200 m Schf. u. Grauw. m. Peltura 500 m		Fran-conian
		Leptoblastus-Eurycare			Alaunschiefer	Olenusschiefer			Lingula					Basische Ergüsse u. Tuffe	Croixian
		Parabolina spinulosa							flags Ffestiniog		cγ				
		Olenus							Maentwrog		Grün-schiefer		Bunte		Dresbachian
		Agnostus pisiformis													
Mittel-kambrium	Paradoxides	Paradoxides forchhammeri			3 m	Andrarums Kalk 20 m	5 m	?	200 m	1000 m	?	50 m Konglomerat von Vosník	Quarzite	100 m Grès à Conocoryphe	Albertan (Acadian)
		Paradoxides paradoxissimus (= tessini)			Alaunschiefer	Paradoxidesschiefer			Menevian	Brek-gruppe (Röros-schiefer)	cβ	400 m Schiefer von Jince u. Skryje	600 m Schiefer u. Sandstein m. Paradoxides	1000 m Schistes à Paradoxides	
		Paradoxides oelandicus						100 m Durnesskalk z.T.	300 m Solva u. Ob. Harlech		Grauwacken	50 m Kongl. u. Sdst. v. Milec u. Tyrovice			
Unter-kambrium	Protolenus					1m Serpulite grit Fucoid beds	25 m 25 m		1000 m	50 m	10 m Protolenusschf. 5 m Eodiscusschf.	1000 m Kongl. v. Tremosna 400 m Grauw. v. Bohutin 200 m Kongl. v. Hlubos	m. 800 m Protolenus u. Eodiscus	Myopsolenus Termierella	50m Schistes à Kingaspis 150m Grès terminaux
					1m Phosphorith.	100 m					cα			
	Holmia	Strenuella linnarssoni		20 m Fukoidensdst.	1m Grauwacken-schf.	25 m Lingulen-sdst.		Pipe Rock	Unt.		500 m	50 m Kongl. v. Zirec	Schiefer u. m. Holmia	Longianda + Gigantopygus	200 m
		Holmia kjerulfi	125 m Baltische St.	15 m Eophytonsdst.	2m Risperbjergsandstein 70 m Grüne Schiefer	30 m Glaukonitsdst.	Michwitzia-sdst.	25 m Harlech	Holmia-schiefer	Archäo-cyathiden-kalk			Bondonella +	Complexe schisteux
		Holmia torelli	200 m Waldai - St.	70 m Blauer Ton 25 m Öberjam-Sch. 100 m Laminariten-Sch.	30 m Nexösandstein	50 m Hardeberga-sdst.		Basal quarzite	2 m Discinellasdst.		Grauwacken	Neltneria	Waucobian (Georgian)
	Discinella holsti			25 m Gdow-Sdst.									Antatlasia	
			100 m Wolhynische St.						?		?		Daguinaspis + Resserops	300 m
									↓ ?				Choubertella	Série schisto-calcaire
													Fallotaspis	
													200m Calcaires supérieurs	
Liegendes:			Archäikum und Algonkium					Torridonian	Algonkium (Sparagmit)		? Algonkium		?	Précambrien III (Calcaires inférieurs)	Proterozoic

grad.The so-called Blue Clay, an alternating sequence of greenish siltstones and sandstones, contains the first marine fossils; it was marginally
replaced by saline variegated silts. From this original basin the transgression moved toward the W. In Sweden sandstone with a few chitino-phos-
phatic brachiopods and traces of bottom-dwelling organisms was laid
down at a later date. Often sandstone-dikes formed which filled the
fractures of the basement opened by weathering. At the end of the Lower
Cambrian a brief regression followed, and soon after a new transgression,
which brought with it a fauna characterized by Paradoxides. The Middle
Cambrian transgression did not spread so far E as that of the Lower
Cambrian, but inundated a part of the ridge which had subdivided the
Baltic epicontinental sea from the Norwegian geosyncline. The Middle-
and Upper Cambrian sea was, like the present-day Baltic, only partly
oxygenated. It gave rise to bituminous, pyritic and calcareous muds, which
turned into Alaunschiefer and bituminous limestones. Fossils, especially
trilobites, abound and permit a widely applicable and detailed subdivision
into zones.

In **eastern Europe** the crystalline basement of the Russian platform,
especially in the NW, W, and SW, is covered by a layer of lowest Cambrian clastic deposits. The strata begin with continental red arkoses, and
in White Russia and Volhynia even with basalts and basaltic tuffs. Toward
the top arenaceous-argillaceous sediments of shallow seas developed,
which have been classified largely as in Estonia. Middle- and Upper
Cambrian is absent from the entire platform.

Western Europe. At the beginning of the Cambrian the Norwegian-
British Caledonian trough, which had bordered the NW-boundary of the
Baltic Shield since the late Algonkian, extended into the middle of Europe.
During the course of the Cambrian there originated here a huge region
of subsidence which was bounded on the N by the Baltic Shield and
extended beyond the Mediterranean sea to the S.

In Brittany and Normandy, the Armorican Massif, subdivision is difficult
because of the absence of fossils; in the Upper Cambrian eruptive rocks
are widespread. In anticlinal cores of the Brabant Massif, in the Ardennes,
and in the Hohe Venn, non-fossiliferous variegated phyllites and quartzites
of Deville and Revin underlie the Ordovician; those of Revin probably
belong to the Cambrian.

It is not until **central Europe,** especially in the classical Bohemian basin,
then in the Franconian Forest, Lausitz, and the Svientokrzyz Range of
central Poland, that one meets a succession which has allowed a complex
classification by its fossil content. The Svientokrzyz Range displays marked
funal affinities with the Baltic. In the Lausitz and in the Franconian Forest
one encounters immigrants from N and S, whereas Bohemia belongs pre-

2 Brinkmann, Geologic Evolution of Europe

dominantly to the region of Mediterranean fauna. The basinal axis of the Cambrian geosyncline extends via the Bober-Katzbach Range to central Poland. Only in this zone is Lower Cambrian known in central Europe. The Middle Cambrian spread north and south from here and marks the highest point the sea reached. The Upper Cambrian is regressive. Generally it consists of sheets of igneous rocks, while in the deepest parts of the trough, in the Lausitz, the basic lavas are especially thick. Cambrian may be still more widely distributed in the central German uplands in the metamorphic state, as phyllite, marble, and green-schists, as in the northwest Thuringian Forest, Taunus, Vorspessart, Fichtelgebirge, in Saxony and in Sudetia.

In the *Bober-Katzbach Range* and near Görlitz, a limestone complex with Archaeocyathus increasing in thickness to 700 m. forms the oldest known fossil horizon. This is overlain by red and green shales with Eodiscus and protolenids. The higher Cambrian is represented by a greenschist sequence more than 1000 m. thick, which is composed chiefly of diabasic rocks.

The section in the *Svientokrzyz Hills,* which is more than 1500 m. thick and includes the whole Cambrian, is distinguished from that in the Bober-Katzbach Range by the preponderance of sandy deposits; limestone is missing.

In the *Lausitz,* as revealed by the boring near Dobrilugk, the Middle Cambrian rests directly on old gneisses. Here we approach the boundary of the geosyncline toward the Baltic Shield, which extends to the subsurface of the east Elbian lowland.

In *Bohemia* the sea first transgressed in the Middle Cambrian, although non-marine sedimentation perhaps began sooner. The old Paleozoic stratal series of the central Bohemian basin, the Barrandian, was deposited in a region of subsidence. This was apparently limited by ridges in the region of the Erzgebirge on one side, and in southern Bohemia on, the other. Meanwhile, the Bohemian sea formed a wide connection with that in central Germany. The fauna of the shales of Jince, which consists of approximately 60 species, shows a close relationship with central and southern Europe, and even further with England and Scandinavia. At the end of the Middle Cambrian the sea retreated from Bohemia and from the Bober-Katzbach Range. The Upper Cambrian is characterized as in Brittany and the Lausitz by the products of vigorous volcanic activity which was marked by somewhat more silicic lavas. The Cambrian of the Franconian Forest displays a close connection with the Bohemian section.

The **Alps** and **Mediterranean region** likewise belonged to the great Cambrian geosyncline. Fossil evidence of the Cambrian has not been found in the Alps, but it may perhaps be hidden in the central Alpine crystalline rocks, e.g. in the quartz phyllite of the eastern Alps and the Casanna schists of Switzerland. Archeocyathid limestones are characteristic of the Mediterranean Lower Cambrian. The Middle Cambrian is chiefly shaly. The Upper Cambrian is sandy and contains basic volcanics, or is lacking altogether. Cambrian is known from the Dead Sea, Sardinia, Montagne Noire, from Asturia and the Celtiberian chains, the Sierra Morena, and southern Portugal, as well as in Morocco.

The fossiliferous section of the Antiatlas in southern *Morocco* reaches an especially deep stratigraphic horizon and forms a transition filling the almost world-wide gap between the Algonkian and Paleozoic. The boundary between Precambrian and Cambrian lies within a thick limestone complex containing Collenia, and is determined by the appearance of the archeocyathids, followed by the first trilobites. A second peculiarity of the Moroccan Lower Cambrian, which it shares with southern Spain and the Dead Sea, is the pronounced East-Asiatic faunal affinity. As early as that the Mediterranean clearly belonged to a world-embracing migration route for marine organisms.

Arctic. The Caledonian trough zone extended via Spitzbergen and eastern and northern Greenland into the archipelago north of Canada. The arctic Cambrian represents a particular area as regards fauna and facies which extends as far as northwest Scotland and the northeastern Appalachians. In the course of the Middle Cambrian the sea withdrew and returned in the Ordovician.

General Features

Climate and environment. The humid temperate climate, which had prevailed over long periods in the Precambrian, reappeared after the infra-Cambrian Ice Age. This is indicated by the facies of the lowest Lower Cambrian which is rich in clastics and poor in limestone. Archeocyathid limestones are characteristic of the higher parts of this stage. Even though the taxonomic position of this group of animals is not entirely clear, it is readily permissible to assume that like the reef-builders of later times, they preferred to live in warm seas. The appearance of evaporitic sediments — for example, the gypsum in Morocco — signifies an increase of temperature.

Crustal movements and magmatism. Between the Algonkian and the Cambrian there was a long period of geocraty from which we have an incomplete record of sedimentation. The Cambrian therefore lies transgressively almost everywhere:

Tremadoc

Upper Cambrian	Transgression (Arctic)
Middle Cambrian	Regression (central and southern Europe) Maximum spread of Cambrian sea Transgression (Northern Europe; Bohemian Massif)
Lower Cambrian	Regression (Northern Europe; Greenland) Transgression (Morocco; northern and northwestern Europe; Greenland)

Algonkian

There were no orogenic movements. The outflow of lavas was limited and increased first in the Upper Cambrian as an introduction to the volcanic epoch of the Ordovician.

Retrospect. During the course of the Cambrian the paleogeographic map changed considerably because of the initiation of a far reaching transgression; on the other hand, the position of the large geosynclines remained the same. A fauna which had become abundant and diverse during the interval since the Algonkian spread with the transgression.

The rocks of the lower Cambrian resemble in their composition the coarse-grained clastics of the Algonkian. Only later did shales and limestones predominate. Perhaps this signified a climatic change — an amelioration after the infra-Cambrian Ice Age.

Supplementary Articles

P. Hupé: Cambrien inférieur et Précambrian III de l'Anti-Atlas Morocain. Mém. Serv. Géol. Maroc. 103. 1952.

R. and E. Richter: Studien im Paläozoikum der Mittelmeerländer. Abh. Senckenb. Naturf. Ges. 450, 455, 460. 1940—1941.

M. Schwarzbach: Vulkanismus und Senkung in der Kaledonischen Geosynklinale Mitteleuropas. Geol. Rundsch. 34, 13. 1943.

A. H. Westergård: Publications on the stratigraphy and the fauna of the Cambrian of Sweden. Sver. Geol. Und. Ca 8 (1922); C 394 (1936); 477 (1946); 489 (1947); 498 (1948); 511 (1950); 526 (1953).

Chapter 4.

Ordovician

Preliminary Remarks

Boundaries and classification. The Silurian, thanks to the first investigations in Wales, was defined at about the same time as the Cambrian. Discoveries of fossils permitted R. I. Murchison, who named it, not only to establish a subdivision into two parts, Lower and Upper Silurian, but also a succession of stages. Most geologists today recognize the two parts as having the rank of systems and, after the suggestion of Ch. Lapworth

(1879), designate the Lower Silurian as Ordovician. Its lower boundary is marked in many places by a short-lived regression, and is characterized by the sudden expansion of many groups which forms a clear contrast with the Cambrian, where siliceous sponges, stromatoporoids, tetracorals, tabulates, clams, calcareous brachiopods, nautiloids, graptolites, crinoids, etc. were few or lacking. A similar stratigraphic break that is associated locally with mountain-building movements separates the Ordovician from the Silurian. A series of characteristic groups, such as the endocerates among the nautiloids, the asaphids and illaenids among the trilobites and the branched graptolites, do not cross the upper boundary of the Ordovician.

Distribution. Cambrian and Ordovician generally follow one another conformably; the outlines of the great geosynclines remained unchanged. The two systems, therefore, have on the whole the same distribution.

The fauna and stratigraphy of the Ordovician of the Baltic lands have been studied in Norway by W. C. Brögger and L. Størmer; in Sweden, by I. G. O. Linnarsson, G. Holm, J. C. Moberg, and P. Thorslund; and in the eastern Baltic by Fr. Schmidt and A. Öpik. In the British Isles Ch. Lapworth, O. T. Jones, and C. J. Stubblefield have continued the tradition of Murchison and Sedgwick. Information of the central European Ordovician has been extended in Bohemia notably by J. Barrande and B. Bouček, and in the central German ranges by R. Richter and H. R. v. Gaertner.

Principal Regions (Fig. 10)

Norwegian Mountains and British Isles. The Cambrian rocks of the Caledonian geosyncline and the Baltic Shield, while of different thicknesses, show the same shaly aspect; but in the Ordovician significant differences appeared. In contrast to the epicontinental sediments, the geosynclinal deposits are uniform, richer in clastic components, and poorer in limestone. Increasing masses of eruptive intercalations also appear. In the lowest Ordovician, the development of "greenstones", submarine andesitic to basaltic lavas and tuffs was widespread. The basic rocks were later replaced by silicic effusives and intrusives. This change in magmatism prefigured the beginning of the Caledonian orogeny, whose first phase fell in the Arenig. In the unstable and complex geosyncline, disturbed by further preliminary folding, predominantly sandy to conglomeratic, flysch-like rocks were deposited.

In the British Isles the Caledonian geosyncline is accessible almost right across its breadth; in Scandinavia, only the eastern half is visible. The sequence at Girvan (southern Scotland) was laid down not far from its northwestern border. This sequence is thick, calcareous to coarsely clastic, and interrupted by some unconformities; it displays many similarities with the deposits of the Trondheim area. In the middle of the basin (Southern Uplands, Lake District, northwest Wales) the beds thin into graptolitic shales, but toward the other margin, in eastern Wales, they become thicker again and coarser grained. As in Norway, volcanic activity reached its maximum in the Arenig-Llandeilo. Submarine basic eruptives with the characteristic pillow structure are widespread.

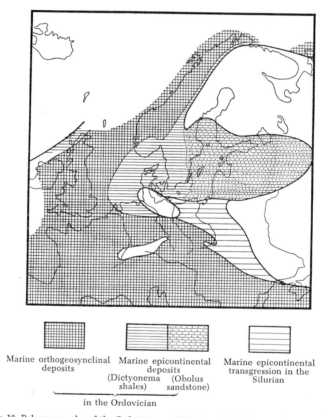

Marine orthogeosynclinal   Marine epicontinental   Marine epicontinental
        deposits   deposits   transgression in the
                              (Dictyonema   (Obolus   Silurian
                                shales)   sandstone)

                              in the Ordovician

Fig. 10. Paleogeography of the Ordovician and Silurian in Northern and Central Europe

Baltic Lands. The tectonic and magmatic instability which began in the Caledonian geosyncline with the Ordovician influenced the foreland. The basement plate of the Baltic Shield underwent lively epeirogenic undulations, which were reflected in a richer variety of facies than that of Cambrian time. A few ash falls originating in the geosyncline were blown over the Baltic area and became embedded as layers of bentonite.

Sediments alternated principally between brachiopod-trilobite limestones and graptolite-shales. The total thickness and proportion of the shale increases, as the Caledonian geosyncline is approached, from E to

W. The Ordovician of Estonia is 150 m. thick and consists almost entirely of pure calcareous material, whereas the section at Oslo measures 350 m. and is nearly half shale. The eastern Baltic was flooded again in the Tremadoc; the Dictyonema zone here rests on the Lower Cambrian in the transgressive facies of the Obolus-sandstone. Throughout almost the whole of the Ordovician this region was covered by especially shallow water. Stratal gaps, submarine solution- and reworking horizons are common. Only in the Kuckers-stage was there a temporary formation of a quiet, closed basin, in which a richly fossiliferous bituminous marl, the Kuckersit, was deposited. The shelf sea in Sweden and southern Norway was deeper than in the eastern Baltic, and the stratal sequence is correspondingly more complete. Västergötland (between the lakes of Wener and Wettern), with its mainly calcareous development, lay on a submarine ridge. Everywhere else dark graptolitic shales predominate.

Central Europe. Just as in the Cambrian, the Norwegian-British Caledonian trough was connected toward the S with a wide complex geosynclinal area, embracing central and western Europe and the Mediterranean. The greatest depth of the central European segment of the basin followed the northern edge of the Ardennes-Rhenish Schiefergebirge. At the beginning of the Ordovician the sea moved E from here, where sedimentation had perhaps continued uninterruptedly from the Cambrian into the Ordovician, and covered again eastern Germany and Bohemia, where non-marine Upper Cambrian had been deposited. The central European basin extended southward to the Alemannic Island (p. 34), and northward to the epicontinentally flooded southern margin of the Baltic Shield, which is thought to constitute the subsurface of northern Germany.

In the *Ardennes* and in the *Brabant Massif* the oldest known fossiliferous horizon belongs to the Tremadoc. The Ordovician consists throughout of a uniform shale; its thickness measures approximately 1000 m. Only the faintly unconformable Caradoc is notably sandy.

In the *Schiefergebirge* east of the Rhine Ordovician rocks occur in two areas. In the Sauerland a section composed almost completely of soft shale is exposed in the cores of the Remscheid and Ebbe anticlines. Near Giessen, on the eastern margin of the Schiefergebirge, only Llandeilo has been recognized as yet; it is noteworthy for its facies, which is more distinctly sandy than that in the Sauerland. It is uncertain whether the sericitic gneiss and greenschist of the Taunus, which are overlain by the Silurian, can be considered as metavolcanics and tuffs of Cambro-Ordovician age.

The key area for understanding of the central European Ordovician is *Bohemia* with its complete, richly fossiliferous, and well studied stratal sequence. The sea returned after the continental period of the Upper Cambrian. Perhaps the transgression came from the N, for the fauna of dα, as in the whole of the older Ordovician, displays a close affinity with the Baltic fauna. The deposits are thickest along the axis of the Barrandian, where the floor of the sea subsided most quickly. The geosynclinal basic volcanism, which culminated in the lower Ordovician as in England and Norway, lasted longest here. Toward the margins of the trough the effusives and tuffs recede; shale is replaced by quartzite; in dγ—dε oölitic chamosite iron ore seams occur, of which the upper Nučic horizon has economic significance. Outside the Barrandian the Ordovician section is developed as a uniform shale, beginning with the Arenig-Llanvirn. This facies can be found in central Bohemia, the Eisengebirge, western Sudetia, and Moravia. Nearly all of Bohemia, therefore, must have been inundated.

The *Franconian Thuringian Schiefergebirge* in its entirety resembles the Bohemian section, both faunally and stratigraphically, but it was petrographically more varied. A thick Tremadoc lies unconformably on the Algonkian; coarse-grained quartzite of the lowest dα, into which extend remains of the Upper Cambrian volcanism. These are overlain by sandy shale and sandstone which derive their name from Phycodes circinatus, the burrow of a worm-like organism. From the Griffel slate on there is an especially close connection with the inner Bohemian basin.

Saxony. In the phyllitic mantle of the Erzgebirge and Granulitgebirge, and in the core of a few more central German ranges, thick, nonfossiliferous and faintly metamorphosed schists and quartzites outcrop; these resemble those recognized in the Franconian-Thuringian Ordovician.

Eastern Germany and Poland. Caledonian movements began very early — between the Cambrian and Ordovician — in northern Saxony, in the Lausitz and Bober-Katzbach Range. The Tremadoc begins with coarse quartzites which are overlaid by sandy shale and diabase. The Svientokrzyz hills of central Poland belong to the same tectonic zone as the Lausitz; here, too, higher Tremadoc rests unconformably on the Cambrian. The later Ordovician consists of moderately thick sandstones and shales with Baltic facies and fauna.

Eastern Alps. In contrast to the western Alps, where intense metamorphism has obscured the pre-Carboniferous stratigraphy, the eastern Alps display an intricately subdivided early-Paleozoic section. It falls into two main parts: the Graywacke zone north of the crystalline central Alps, and the Carnic Alps and Graz mountains to the south. The sandy Caradoc is the oldest biostratigraphically determined horizon in the Carnic Alps. Unfossiliferous series containing quartz porphyries are widespread

Ordovizium

	Leitende Graptolithen		Baltischer Schild				Kaledonische Geosynkline				Mitteleuropäische Geosynkline							Nord-amerika	
	Zonen n. Elles-Wood	Gattungen	Estland	Västergötland	Schonen	Oslo	Norweg. Hochgeb.	Schottland	England Lake District	England Ostwales	Ardennen u. Massiv v. Brabant	Rhein. Schiefergebirge Ebbe	Rhein. Schiefergebirge Giessen	Unterharz	Thüring. Schiefergeb.	Böhmen	Karnische Alpen		
Hangendes:			F₂ Borkholmsch.	*Llandovery* (Dalmanitesschiefer)		5b Sch.m. *Meristella crassa*	(Horggr.) *Llandovery*	(Birkhill shales)	(Stockdale shales)	(Llandovery series)	Llandovery (Ass. de Grand-Manil)	Ludlow (Köbbingh.Sch.)	Wenlock (Ostracod-kalk)	(Harzgeröder Sch.)	*Llandovery* (Untere Graptolith. schf.)	(Sch.v.Liteň)	(Krinoidenk.) eα	Silurian (Albion)	Ashgill
Ashgill	15	Climaco-	F₁ Lyckholmsch. 80 m	25 m Tretaspisschf. (Trinucleusschf.)	Ob. Tretaspisstufe	5a Ob.Chasmops-zone 30 m	500 m Ob.	900 m	30 m Ashgill series	700 m Ashgill series	100 m Assise de Fosse	250 m Obere		Ottrelith-	450 m Sch.v.Kosov Zdice Sch.v.Králův Dvůr	dγ	10 m Tonflaserk.	Richmondian	Cincinnatian
	14	graptus Dicrano-	E Wesenberg- (Rakvere-) Sch. 5 m		Chasmopsstufe	100 m Trinucleuskalk und -schiefer 120 m	Ob. Hovin-gruppe	Ard-millan	Hartfell		600 m Assises de Gembloux et Fauquex	Ton-schiefer		u.	Leder- Sch.v. Nučice	500 m	50 m Schiefer u.	Maysvillian	
	13	u. graptus	D₃ Wasalemm-(Vasalemma-)Sch. 10 m			Dicello- 90 m			200 m Coniston series	200 m Caradoc				Zone des Ostharzes	schiefer Zaho-řany		Quarzite	Edenian	Mohawkian Caradoc
Caradoc	12	Ortho- graptus	D₂ Kegel-(Keila-)Sch. 10 m	20 m	Mittl. graptus-schiefer	Chasmops-kalk	1000 m Unt.	series	series		series				dε Zaho-řany dε₂	Sch.v. Chrustenice		Utica	
	11	u. Dicello- graptus	D₁ Jewe-(Jõhvi-)Sch. 10m	Chasmops-kalk		u.-schiefer					100 m Assises de Vitriol-Bruyière et de Rigenée	300 m Grau-wacken-schiefer	Quarzit von Andreas-teich	Karpho-	dε₁	100 m		Trenton	
	10		C₃ Jtfer-(Jdavere-)Sch. 1m		Unt.	45 m Ampyx-Kalk			3000 m Borrow-					lith-	Haupt-quarzit	Quarzit v. Drabov		Black River	
	9	Nema- graptus	C₂ Kukkers-(Kukruse-)Sch. 10m				200 m Barr-series	10m Glen-kiln sh.	dale					schiefer	5 m Ob. Erzhorizont	dδ	?		
Llandeilo	8		c 5m Uhaku-Kalk C,b 10m Tallinna Echinosphäritenk.	50 m		10m Bronni-Sch. 10m Ogygiocaris-Schf.			volcanic series	250 m Ob. Llandeilo series						300 m dγ₂₋₃		Chazyan	
Llanvirn	7		a Aseri Ob.		Asaphusstufe	40 m Obere Didymograptus-schiefer				500 m Llanvirn series	100 m Assises de Sart-Bernard et de Huy	150 m Unt. Ton-schiefer		Schichten v. Osek u. Kváň	120 m Griffel-schiefer u. Mittl.	dγ₁			
	6	Didymo-	B₃ Vaginatenkalk 6 m	Ortho-ceren-								Pletten-berger		Quar-ziten mit	Erzhorizont				
Arenig	5	graptus Phyllo- graptus	B₂ Glaukonitkalk 4 m	kalk	Ob. Didymo-graptus-schiefer	c' Endoceras-Asaphus-Megalaspis-Kalk 10m	2000 m Stören-(Bymark-)	500 m Basische	Skiddaw slates	700 m Arenig series		Bänder-schiefer		100 m Schichten v. Komárov	dβ 3 m Unt.		Beekman-town	Canadian Arenig
	4	u. Tetra-		Unt.	Unt.	10m Unt. Didymogr. schiefer		Laven						Metamorphe	Erzhorizont				
	3	graptus	B₁ Glaukonitsand 1m			1m Ceratopygekalk	gruppe	u.Tuffe		1000 m	400 m				700 m Phycodensch.	50 m			
Tremadoc	2	Bryograptus	A₃ 2m Dictyonema-schiefer	2 m Ceratopygekalk u.-schiefer	2 m Ceratopyge-schiefer	10m Ceratopygeschf.		?		Shineton shales	Assise Salmien			Klippmühl-	da Krušnáhora-			Gasconade	Tremadoc
	1	Dictyonema	A₂ Obolensdst. 3m	1m Dictyonema-schiefer	10 m Dictyonema-schiefer	2e Dictyonema-schf. 9m	Brek-gruppe	?			?			quarzit 600 m Frauenbach-schichten	schichten		?		
Liegendes:			A₁ Unterkambrium (Fukoidensdst.)	Oberkambrium (Olenusschiefer)				?		Oberkambr. (Lingula flags)	? Kambrium (Revinien)			? Kambr.	Algonkium	cγ Oberkambr. (Sch.v.Ohrazenice)		Oberkambr. (Trempealeauan)	

throughout the Graywacke zone; they recall the Thuringian Tremadoc and the Lausitzian Cambrian.

Western and southwestern Europe, North Africa. The most important areas for Ordovician are Brittany, Montagne Noire, the massif of Mouthoumet, the Pyrenees, Asturia, the Celtiberian chains, Sierra Morena, and Sardinia, which link up with Morocco and the Sahara on the other side of the Mediterranean. Tremadoc is absent in many localities; instead the Armorican quartzite (Arenig) transgresses over the often gently-folded Cambrian.

General Features

Climate and environment. In contrast with the Cambrian, in which shales predominate, the lower Ordovician is mostly sandy, whereas toward the top of the system the proportion of calcareous facies increases, either in the form of fine-grained or oölitic limestones, or in the form of organogenic rocks composed of calcareous algae, brachiopods, bryozoa, or echinoderms. The opposite pole to these deposits of a shallow sea is represented by the dark-colored, evenly laminated graptolitic shales, which originated on the floor of a poorly ventilated euxinitic marine basin. Widespread oölitic iron ores are characteristic of the Ordovician; these occur in Bohemia, Thuringia, Brittany and in the northern parts of the Iberian peninsula. This evidence suggests that the Ordovician must have had a relatively mild climate with slowly rising temperatures.

Crustal movements and magmatism. After the tectonically stable period of the Cambrian with the Ordovician began a time of active crustal movements. A series of orogenic phases which first came to a peak in the transition Ordovician-Silurian, determined the progress of events:

Llandovery

	∼∼∼∼∼∼∼∼∼Taconic phase of folding
Ashgill	Widespread regression
Caradoc	Maximum spread of Ordovician seas
Llandeilo and Llanvirn	Transgression (British Isles, Norway, southwest Europe, Arctic)
Arenig	Transgression (southwest Europe)
Tremadoc	Transgression (Bohemia, central Germany, Eastern Baltic, Arctic)

Upper Cambrian

In the Ordovician the central and northern European region of subsidence experienced the stage of geosynclinal volcanism; the lava outflow reached a maximum, particularly in the Arenig.

Plate 2. Ordovician index fossils

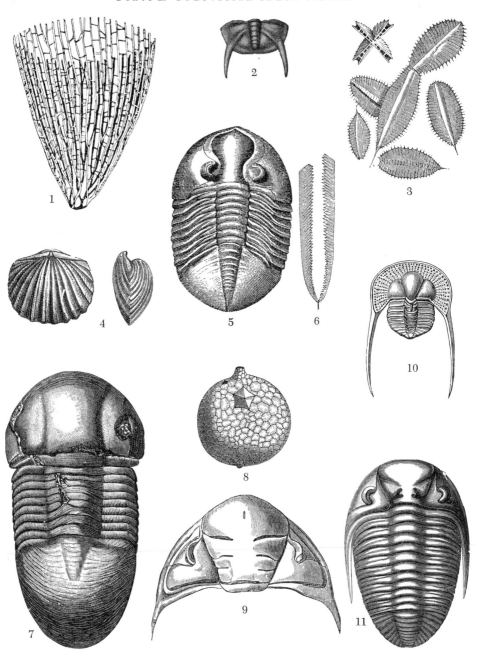

Tremadoc: 1. *Dictyonema flabelliforme* EICHW. 2. *Ceratopyge forficula* SARS. Arenig: 3. *Phyllograptus typus* HALL. Llanvirn: 4. *Orthis calligramma* DALM. 5. *Asaphus expansus* WAHL. 6. *Didymograptus murchisoni* BECK. Llandeilo: 7. *Illaenus oblongatus* ANG. 8. *Echinosphaera aurantium* HISING. Caradoc: 9. *Dalmanitina socialis* BARR. 10. *Cryptolithus goldfussi* BARR. 11. *Chasmops odini* EICHW.

Retrospect. A warm climate prevailed even into high latitudes. Under its influence numerous new groups of invertebrates evolved, in particular those with calcareous shells, so that for the first time extensive organogenic calcareous deposits originated. Tectonically and magmatically the Ordovician heralded the forthcoming Caledonian orogeny. In the dimensions of its seas, the varied facies, and the volcanic activity it outpasses the Cambrian.

Supplementary articles

O. T. Jones. On the evolution of a geosyncline: Quart. J. 94, LX. 1938.

Kl. Sdzuy: Die Fauna der Leimitz-Schiefer (Tremadoc). Abh. Senck. Natf. Ges. 492. 1955.

Chapter 5.

Silurian (Gotlandian)

Preliminary Remarks

Boundaries and classification. It is usual today to use the term Silurian only for the latest part of Murchison's Silurian system (p. 20). The name Gotlandian, which Ch. Lapworth (1879) proposed in order to avoid ambiguity, has not been accepted.

At the base of the Silurian there is a widespread stratigraphic gap, which here and there is marked by an unconformity. For this reason the Silurian fauna seems to appear rather abruptly. The Caledonian orogenesis, the first great Paleozoic mountain-building epoch, forms a natural break at the end of this period.

Distribution. The Silurian generally rests, as stated, conformably on the Ordovician, but is often transgressive. Therefore, while both systems are similarly distributed, the later one also occupies other areas.

The Baltic region is fundamental for understanding the Silurian: Sweden (N. Angelin, G. Lindström), Norway (J. Kiaer), and the eastern Baltic (Fr. Schmidt). The structure and stratigraphy of the Norwegian mountains has been described by A. E. Törnebohm, O. Holtedahl, V. M. Goldschmidt, and Th. Vogt. In Great Britain G. L. Elles, whose name is also associated with the Ordovician, has contributed to the Silurian. In Bohemia, A. Přibyl has continued the research of Barrande. In the central ranges of Germany, A. Denckmann, R. Richter, F. Dahlgrün have studied the Silurian; F. Frech and F. Heritsch have done the same for the eastern Alps.

Principal Regions (Fig. 10—11)

Norwegian Mountains and British Isles. As early as the Ordovician the geosyncline had been affected by forerunners of Caledonian folding. Soon after the beginning of the Silurian the sea retreated, for no beds more

recent than the Llandovery have been discovered. This regression marked
the onset of the main folding.

In the British Isles the pattern of facies remained unaltered during the
Silurian — shales in the inner basin and calcareous and clastic deposits
along the margins. This pattern was gradually obliterated as over the
course of time the sea became shallower. In the Ludlow it is no longer
possible to distinguish the graptolitic and shellytrilobite facies from one
another. Simultaneously a transgression proceeded beyond the southeastern
edge, which gave rise to richly fossiliferous reef deposits, notably in the
Wenlock in central England. Geosynclinal volcanism during the Silurian
had almost disappeared.

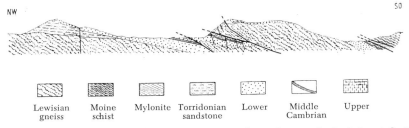

Fig. 11. Marginal overthrust of the Caledonian Mountains on the northwestern foreland. Assynt, Scottish
Highlands. Scale 1 : 175 000, vertical exaggeration 1 · 5 times (after J. Phemister)

The principal folding took place toward the end of the Silurian. In
Scandinavia the axial zone of the orogene followed more or less along
the present Atlantic coast; the rocks here comprise normally folded but
widely migmatized Sparagmite and Cambro-Silurian. The gradually cooling igneous masses together with their sedimentary mantle migrated outward from this central zone toward the SE and moved over the margin
of the Baltic Shield in the form of low-angle thrust sheets. The counterpart
of the Scandinavian mountain overthrust is the Moine Thrust of northern
Scotland, on which the movement was directed toward the NW, toward
the Hebrides Massif (Fig. 11). In northern England and Wales sediments
measuring up to 12 000 m. thick were forced into fairly regular folds,
which gradually decrease in size toward the SE. Uplift and erosion began
with the orogenesis. But very soon, partly even in the Upper Ludlow,
areas of subsidence appeared within the rising mountains, smaller in Norway, larger in the British Isles. These filled with red terrestrial waste
products, which introduced the Devonian sequence of the Old Red
(p. 39).

Baltic Lands. On the Baltic Shield the Silurian everywhere transgressively follows a break which corresponds to one of the preliminary orogenic
phases of the geosynclinal through. The facies pattern resembles that of

the Ordovician, but was even more varied in the Silurian owing to the occurrence of reefs and associated rocks as well as brackish and saline precipitates. A deep trough that follows the modern Baltic formed a new tectonic element to some extent replacing the Caledonian geosyncline which had now become a land area. On Gotland this trough was filled by more than 500 m. of richly fossiliferous marls containing lenses of reef limestone; rocks of similar thickness have been bored on the east Pomeranian coast. What is now Estonia belonged as in the Ordovician to the shallowest part of the sea covering the Baltic Shield. It is here, landward from the reef zone Gotland-Ösel-Dagö, that in the later Silurian lagoonal dolomites with eurypterids and fish were deposited; even salt occurs in thin beds. Southwest of the reef girdle one enters the region of graptolite facies, but near Oslo richly fossiliferous nodular and reef limestones occur again. During the course of the Ludlow the sea gradually withdrew from the Baltic region. Either sedimentation ended on the one hand, or variegated sandstones and shales with a brackish to fresh-water fauna of lingulids, eurypterids and fish on the other, replace the marine beds.

Central Europe, during the early Paleozoic, belonged to a geosyncline which was created in the Lower Cambrian and was widened by the transgressions of the Middle Cambrian and the Tremadoc. Its northern border with the Baltic Shield more or less follows the line of the Elbe in the subsurface of the north German lowland. The Alemannic island (p. 34) formed the border on the opposite side. The Silurian sea was contained within these limits, but was deeper and more uniform than in the Ordovician as shown by the widespread sedimentation of graptolitic shales. Toward the end of the Silurian a lateral branch of the large Caledonian orogene was folded along the northern border of the Central European geosyncline and narrowed the connection to the N. The fold-chain stretched in a wide arc from the Ardennes to Sudetia toward the E and enclosed Bohemia and Thuringia as an unfolded area. Parts of this chain were uplifted and rigidified. In the Middle Ludlow the remainder sank under a new transgression which initiated the Variscan geosyncline (p. 34).

The *Ardennes* region was affected by the Caledonian orogeny with an intensity that decreased toward the S. In the northern part, the Brabant Massif was consolidated and uplifted, whereas the Ardennes themselves returned again to a geosynclinal state. The Brabant Massif is today almost completely covered by the Tertiary of northern Belgium. The eastward continuation of the Caledonian fold-tract, which is believed to exist in the subsurface of the Netherlands and coastal regions of northwestern Germany, is still more deeply buried. There is only indirect evidence of this based on the discovery of pebbles of Silurian lydite in the Upper Carboniferous of the Ruhr and at Osnabrück.

The northern part of the *Schiefergebirge* east of the Rhine occupies a special position because of its incomplete section. In the Sauerland the middle Ludlow transgresses the gently-folded Ordovician. On the eastern margin of the Schiefergebirge, on the other hand, the Silurian, even though it is moderately thickly developed, is without breaks. Limestone with a Bohemian fauna is found near Giessen, while in the Kellerwald graptolitic shales and cherts predominate.

The succession in the *Harz* and particularly in the Unterharz, where pre-Devonian alone has been recognized, extends from the lower Llandovery to the boundary with the Devonian. This section is distinguished from that in Thuringia by its greater thickness and numerous intercalations of graywackes and quartzites in the graptolitic shales. A region of erosion must have lain north of the Harz which was at the same time responsible for the fairly sharp faunal division of northern Europe. The fauna of the Harz in the lower Silurian stands beween the English and Bohemian. The calcareous lenses which occur in the Ludlow contain fossils with almost pure Bohemian affinities. At the end of the Silurian the strata were thrown into gentle folds transgressed by the Lower Devonian.

In *Bohemia,* after a short interval of uplift and stratigraphic break, the Silurian began with deep subsidence. Then followed a gradual shallowing that lasted until the Devonian and coincided with a gradually decreasing interchange with the North European faunal region. By a steady increase in carbonate content the black graptolitic shales of the Llandovery gave way to the gray bedded limestones of the Ludlow. Besides the bedded rocks, reef facies, in the form of gray massive limestone, occurred from the Ludlow on, characteristically first in the NW. Its extent remained limited in the Silurian but with the beginning of the Devonian it suddenly increased. Silurian has been identified not only in the inner Bohemian depression, but also in the Isergebirge, Eisengebirge and in Moravia. Almost all Bohemia must therefore have been covered by the sea.

The sea did not grow so shallow in the *Franconian-Thuringian Schiefergebirge* as in Bohemia. Black shales and lydites continued to predominate. Bedded limestone appears later than in Bohemia, mainly in the middle Ludlow; reef limestone is entirely lacking. Silurian and Devonian are conformable.

The conformity between Ordovician, Silurian and Devonian continues toward *Saxony.* Caledonian movements become visible at first in the Elbe valley region and from there increase eastwards.

Eastern Germany and Poland. In the Lausitz and in the Bober-Katzbach Range the Silurian is faintly transgressive. The moderately thick lydites contain graptolites of the Llandovery and Wenlock. Similar and for the

Silur (Gotlandium)

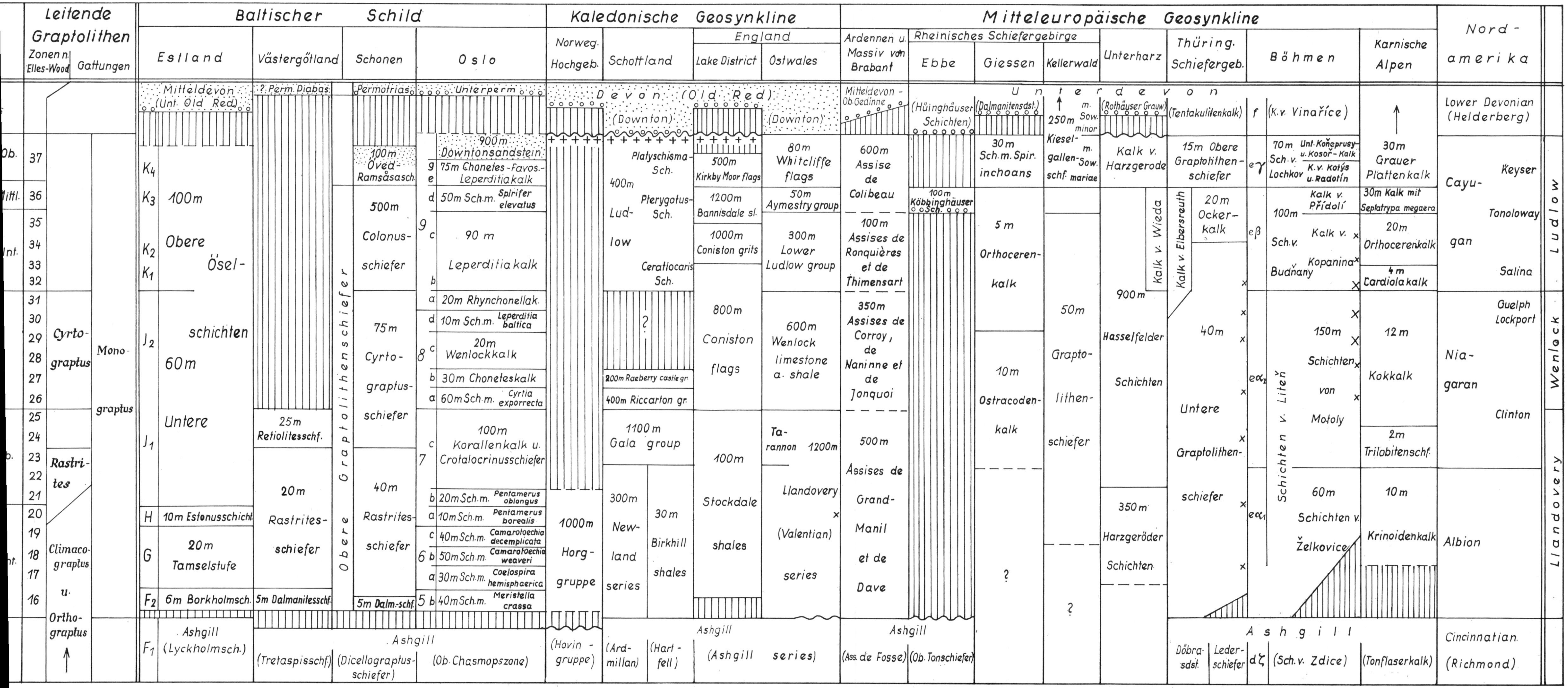

Leitende Graptolithen		Baltischer Schild				Kaledonische Geosynkline					Mitteleuropäische Geosynkline							Nord-amerika	
Zonen n. Elles-Wood	Gattungen	Estland	Västergötland	Schonen	Oslo	Norweg. Hochgeb.	Schottland	Lake District (England)	Ostwales (England)	Ardennen u. Massiv von Brabant	Ebbe (Rheinisches Schiefergebirge)	Giessen	Kellerwald	Unterharz	Thüring. Schiefergeb.	Böhmen	Karnische Alpen	Nord-amerika	
		Mitteldevon (Unt. Old Red)	? Perm Diabas	Permotrias	Unterperm	Devon (Old Red) — (Downton)		(Downton)		Mitteldevon – Ob. Gedinne	(Hüinghäuser Schichten)	(Dalmanitensdst.)	Unterdevon	(Rothäuser Grauw.)	(Tentakulitenkalk) f	(K. v. Vinařice)		Lower Devonian (Helderberg)	
Ob. 37	K4	100 m Obere Ösel- schichten 60 m Untere	100 m Öved-Ramsåsasch.	100 m Downtonsandstein g 75 m Chonetes-Favos.-Leperditiakalk	Platyschisma-Sch.	500 m Kirkby Moor flags	80 m Whitcliffe flags	600 m Assise de Colibeau	30 m Sch.m. Spir. inchoans	Kiesel- gallen- schf.	Kalk v. Harzgerode	15 m Obere Graptolithen-schiefer	70 m Unt. Koněprusy- u. Kosoř-Kalk; K. v. Kotýs u. Radotín eγ	30 m Grauer Plattenkalk	Keyser	Cayu-gan			
Mittl. 36	K3		500 m Colonus-schiefer	d 50m Sch.m. Spirifer elevatus		1200 m Bannisdale sl.	50 m Aymestry group	100 m Assises de Ronquières et de Thimensart	5 m Orthoceren-kalk	Sow. minor m. Sow. mariae	Kalk v. Wieda	20 m Ockerkalk	Kalk v. Přídolí eβ Sch.v.	30m Kalk mit Septatrypa megaera	Tonoloway				
Unt. 35 34 33 32	K2 K1			90 m Leperditia kalk	Ludlow	1000 m Coniston grits	300 m Lower Ludlow group				Kalk v. Elbersreuth		Kalk v. Kopanina Budňany	20 m Orthocerenkalk 4 m Cardiola kalk	Salina				
31 30 29 28 27 26	Mono- graptus J2	schichten	75 m Cyrto-graptus-schiefer	a 20m Rhynchonellak. d 10m Sch.m. Leperditia baltica 20m Wenlockkalk c 30m Choneteskalk b a 60m Sch.m. Cyrtia exporrecta	? 800 m Coniston flags	350 m Assises de Corroy, de Naninne et de Jonquoi	600 m Wenlock limestone a. shale	50 m	Grapto-lithen-schiefer	900 m	40 m Untere Graptolithen-schiefer	150 m Schichten von Motoly eα2	12 m Kokkalk	Nia-garan		Guelph Lockport		
25 24 23 22 21 20 19 18 17 16	Cyrto-graptus graptus Rastri-tes Climaco-graptus u. Ortho-graptus	60 m Untere 10m Estonusschicht 20 m Tamselstufe 6m Borkholmsch.	25 m Retiolitesschf. 20 m Rastrites-schiefer 5m Dalmanitesschf.	c 100m Korallenkalk u. Crotalocrinusschiefer 7 40 m Rastrites-schiefer b 20m Sch.m. Pentamerus oblongus a 10m Sch.m. Pentamerus borealis c 40m Sch.m. Camarotoechia decemplicata b 50m Sch.m. Camarotoechia weaveri a 30m Sch.m. Coelospira hemisphaerica 5m Dalm.-schf. b 40m Sch.m. Meristella crassa	1100 m Gala group 300 m Newland series 1000 m Horg-gruppe	30 m Birkhill shales	100 m Stockdale shales	Ta-rannon 1200 m Llandovery (Valentian) series	500 m Assises de Grand-Manil et de Dave	Hasselfelder Schichten Ostracoden-kalk 10 m	350 m Harzgeröder Schichten	Untere Graptolithen-schiefer 350 m	60 m Schichten v. Želkovice eα1	2 m Trilobitenschf. 10 m Krinoidenkalk	Clinton Albion			
Ortho-graptus ↑		F1 (Lyckholmsch.) Ashgill	5m Dalmanitesschf. (Tretaspisschf.)	(Ob. Chasmopszone) Ashgill (Dicellograptus-schiefer)	(Hovin-gruppe)	(Ard-millan)	(Hart-fell)	Ashgill (Ashgill series)	Ashgill (Ass. de Fosse)	(Ob. Tonschiefer)	? ?		Ashgill Döbra-sdst. dζ Leder-schiefer (Sch. v. Zdice)	(Tonflaserkalk)	Cincinnatian (Richmond)			

Ludlow · Wenlock · Llandovery (vertical labels at right margin)

most part non-fossiliferous series occur in the uplands of Sudetia and the Silesian plain. The unconformable contact with the Devonian indicates that here too the main folding took place during the Caledonian era. The ascent of plutonic rocks (serpentine, gabbro, granite-gneiss) was linked to the folding. The Svientokrzyz Hills of Poland resemble the Lausitz and Silesia in their facies and structure.

In the **eastern Alps** both Silurian limestone and shaly facies are found. In the Carnic Alps limestone is particularly widespread. It appears here considerably earlier than in the Barrandian and is connected with the overlying, but equally calcareous Devonian. Near Graz and in the northern Alpine graywacke zone shales, cherts and graywackes predominate.

Western and southwestern Europe, North Africa. As in the Caledonian- and central European geosyncline, the Silurian of western and south-western Europe is formed chiefly of dark graptolitic shales. Only in the Ludlow does limestone become widespread. Caledonian crustal movements are almost completely lacking. The "Grès inferieurs" spread widely over the North African desert tableland from the southern margin of the geosyncline. These sandstones extend downward into the Ordovician and are overlain by Silurian graptolitic shales.

General features

Climate and environment. The temperature increase which had begun in the Ordovician reached a peak in the upper Silurian. The proportion of carbonate sediment of inorganic as well as organic origin once again increased, and especially important, for the first time in Earth history, coral reefs were widespread. Other deposits correspondingly declined in extent. Graptolitic shales are less abundant than in the Ordovician; oölitic iron deposits receded entirely. Toward the end of the Silurian the climate became more arid. In the eastern Baltic salt deposits are found.

Crustal movements and magmatism. The era of folding which began in the Ordovician reached its peak and conclusion at the end of the Silurian:

Lower Devonian

	～～～～～～～～Ardennes folding phase (Caledonian Mountains, Ardennes, Sudetia)
Ludlow	Regression (Northern Europe, British Isles, Arctic)
	Transgression (Ardennes, Rhenish Schiefergebirge)
Wenlock	Maximum spread of Silurian seas
	Transgression (central England, Arctic)
Llandovery	Transgression (Northern and central Europe; North Africa)
Ashgill	～～～～～～～～Taconic folding phase

Plate 3. Silurian index fossils

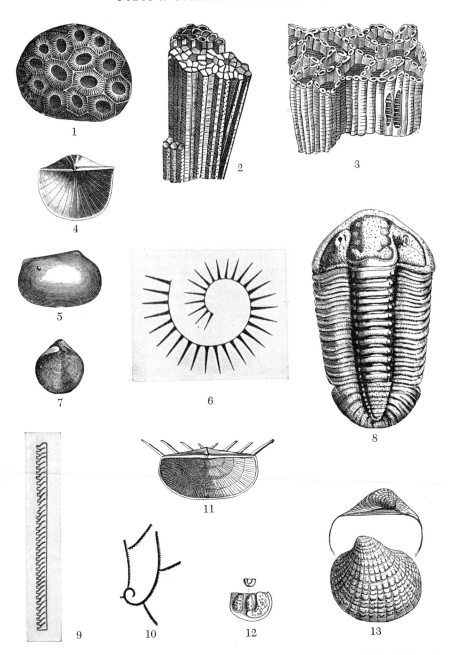

Whole Silurian: 1. *Acervularia ananas* LINN. 2. *Favosites gotlandicus* LINN. 3. *Halysites catenularia* LINN. 4. *Sowerbyella transversalis* DALM. Llandovery: 5. *Leperditia hisingeri* FR. SCHMIDT. 6. *Rastrites linnaei* BARR. Wenlock: 7. *Dalmanella (Parmorthis) elegantula* DALM. 8. *Calymene blumenbachi* BRONGN. 9. *Monograptus priodon* BRONN. 10. *Cyrtograptus murchisoni* CARR. Ludlow: 11. *Chonetes striatella* DALM. 12. *Beyrichia tuberculata* KLOED. 13. *Cardiola cornucopiae* GOLDF.

The Caledonian trough, which extended from the Brabant Massif via Wales and Norway to East Greenland, was folded into the Caledonian chain. It joined the Baltic-Russian platform with the North Atlantic Massif, which today, except for the Hebrides, has sunk into the sea. In this way an extensive mainland, which reached from the English Channel to the Arctic, originated. Its further history belongs to the Devonian.

Retrospect. The Silurian offers a remarkable parallel between the history of the Earth and the development of Life. At the beginning the sea transgressed considerably, and this gave more room to an abundant fauna. Toward the end of the period, with the approach of the chief Caledonian folding, the surface of the land increased and exactly at the same time scorpions, centipedes, and above all the vascular plants, moved onto and began to colonize it.

Supplementary Articles

H. R. v. Gaertner: Erwägungen über präpermische Gebirgszusammenhänge im Untergrund von Norddeutschland. Geol. Jb. 64, 123. 1950.

O. Holtedahl: The structural history of Norway and its relation to Great Britain. Quart. J. 108, 65. 1952.

W. Kegel: Das Paläozoikum der Lindener Mark bei Gießen. Abh. Hess. L.A. Bodenf. 7. 1953.

A. Münch: Die Graptolithen aus dem anstehenden Gotlandium Deutschlands und der Tschechoslowakei. Geologica 7. 1952.

R. and E. Richter: Die Trilobiten des Ebbe-Sattels. Abh. Senckenb. Naturf. Ges. 488. 1954.

Chapter 6.

Devonian

Preliminary Remarks

Boundaries and classification. In the years 1830—1839, H. de la Beche surveyed the hills in southwest England (Devonshire and Cornwall). Murchison and Sedgwick (1839), taking his results and the paleontologic researches of W. Lonsdale, recognized that the majority of the rocks were later than Silurian, but earlier than the Carboniferous. They named the new formation the "Devonian system" and at once ascribed to it the "Old Red Sandstone" of Scotland despite its totally different facies. Soon after they identified strata of the same age in the central German uplands and in Russia. From these stimuli by the middle of the 19th century, the fundamental research into the subdivision and fossil content of the Devonian had grown up as a result of the work of E. Beyrich and F. Roemer in the Rhenish Schiefergebirge, of F. A. Roemer in the Harz, and of A. Dumont in the Ardennes.

3 Brinkmann, Geologic Evolution of Europe

The Devonian as defined today exhibits special features, particularly in its cephalopod and fish fauna as well as in its flora. The lower boundary is recognized by the appearance of new brachiopods, even where the Caledonian folding does not show a clear line of demarcation. The rich expansion of the Carboniferous flora forms an excellent upper dividing line.

Distribution. The map of Europe, especially in the north, was fundamentally altered by the Caledonian mountain building and the regional uplift related to it. The Baltic-Russian Shield, the Caledonian mountains, the Hebrides mass, and Greenland were amalgamated into an extensive block, whose southern coast reached from southern Ireland across Cornwall and Belgium to the hills of central Poland. Non-marine deposits are widespread on this "Old Red continent", and have been studied especially in the British Isles (A. Geikie, R. Traquair, W. H. Lang, and W. W. King), in northern Europe and in the Arctic (A. G. Nathorst, J. Kiaer, O. Holtedahl, and E. Stensiö), and in Russia (C. Grewingk, P. Venjukoff, and W. Gross). S of this area, in central and southern Europe, marine Devonian occurs, to which belong the deposits of the Ardennes (J. Gosselet, Ch. Barrois, E. Maillieux, and E. Asselberghs), the Rhenish Schiefergebirge (F. and G. Sandberger, H. v. Dechen, E. Kayser, A. Denckmann, R. Wedekind, and W. Kegel), the Harz (E. Kayser, M. Koch, and L. Beushausen), Bohemia (J. Barrande, R. Kettner, and F. Prantl), the eastern Alps (F. Frech and F. Heritsch), the Mediterranean lands, and the Urals (Th. Tchernishev).

Principal Regions (Figs. 12—13)

In **central Europe** the Caledonian folding did not reach the same extent as in the N. More significant and widespread was the simultaneous transformation of the epeirogenic structure, which revealed itself in a changed paleogeography and in the variation in sedimentation. Shortly before the transition to the Devonian, the Variscan geosyncline was divided from the wide central European seaway of the Silurian; this area of subsidence was bounded on the N by the Old Red continent, and on the S by the Alemannic-Bohemian island. From the Variscan geosyncline were born the Variscan Mountains of the Late Paleozoic. Only the inner part of the trough was flooded at the beginning of the Devonian. Later the sea grew permanently wider by transgressing its northern and southern margins, but at the same time it became subdivided into two parts by the elevation of the Central German axis, an elongated geanticline which extended from the Saar region to the Lausitz. The facies of the Devonian rocks corresponded to this paleogeographical setting. The Lower Devonian consists predominantly of graywacke, quartzite, and graywacke

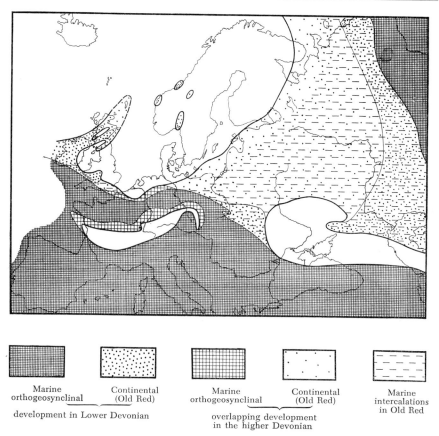

Marine orthogeosynclinal	Continental (Old Red)	Marine orthogeosynclinal	Continental (Old Red)	Marine intercalations in Old Red

development in Lower Devonian   overlapping development
                                       in the higher Devonian

Fig. 12. Paleogeography of the Devonian in Europe

shales. Variegated clastic material from the nearby land, particularly from the northern Old Red continent, is widespread; limestone, however, is almost totally absent. The grain size diminished in the Middle Devonian; soft shales and marls now become common. Deposits of a volcano-interspersed coral sea — reef limestone, lava and tuff, and sedimentary iron ores, appear in the upper Middle Devonian as well. The Upper Devonian lacks the thick, uniform depositional sequences, such as the older Devonian displays, that characterize geosynclinal tracts. The individual sequences are thinner and are sharply separated petrographically; limestone and shale predominate.

The entire Devonian rock column, which measures more than 5000 m., was deposited in essentially conformable arrangement. The few feeble intra-Devonian phases of folding had only local significance. But, nevertheless sedimentation proceeded neither uniformly nor continuously. Permanent undulations in the sinking floor of the geosyncline caused the zone of maximum thickness to be displaced by stages. Many of the Variscan folds displayed themselves in embryonic form even during the Devonian (Fig. 13). Magmatic activity was occasionally very lively. In the Lower Devonian, particularly in the Emsian, quartz keratophyres and related tuffs were intercalated. These effusions ceased at the beginning of the Middle Devonian and were replaced by a more basic series, which was, however, also of Atlantic composition. It reached its maximum in the Givetian and ended in the Adorfian stage. The latest Upper Devonian is almost devoid of volcanic deposits.

The Variscan geosyncline was inhabited by a uniform fauna, which was distributed according to ecologic groups. Brachiopods and pelecypods were the chief inhabitants on sandy-muddy bottoms; rocks and fossils show a Rhenish development. On the other hand, calcareous deposits contain more cephalopods and immigrants from Bohemia where a similar facies developed. These are called Bohemian or Hercyn deposits (p. 37). The two faunal districts were very sharply divided from each other, particularly in the Lower Devonian, but later the differences diminished. In the coastal parts of the geosyncline, especially toward the northern Old Red continent where red clastics increase, the molluscan fauna was reduced to a few mussels. Instead of these, a lagoonal assemblage of armored fish and eurypterids with drifted vascular plants occurs.

The *Ardennes-Rhenish Schiefergebirge* reveals the Variscan geosyncline for almost its entire width and at the same time offers the best insight into its history, which begins with the Ludlow transgression and extends through the Devonian into the Carboniferous.

In the Lower Devonian the axis of the trough lay in the southern part of the Schiefergebirge. The thick sequence of the Hunsrück shales with their splendidly preserved fossils originated here. The Hunsrück shales interfinger toward the N with the sandy Siegen beds and toward the S, with the white quartzite of the Hunsrück-Taunus crest. The eastern part of the Schiefergebirge, near Giessen and in the Kellerwald, was involved in the subsidence of the Variscan trough only slowly. The Lower Devonian here was deposited in a Hercyn facies as a thin, incomplete, and partly calcareous sequence (Fig. 13).

In the Middle Devonian, this configuration became smoother. As in the Lower Devonian, the coarser-grained detrital sediments from the northern continent came to rest in the northwestern part of the area, and the finer-grained material in the central part. Toward the eastern margin the strata become relatively thin and contain calcareous lenses with a Bohemian fauna. In the upper Middle Devonian the sea grew shallower. Coral reefs spread over almost the entire Schiefergebirge and are connected with submarine effusives and marine tuffs, the Schalstein. Albite-rich sodakeratophyre-spilites came to the surface. Iron-rich emanations associated with the eruptions precipitated hematitic ore beds.

In the Upper Devonian the facies contrast was again sharpened by the increasing epeirogenic undulations of the sea floor. Thick Cypridine beds containing ostracods represent the basin (Becken) facies, thin goniatite-rich nodular limestones the ridge (Schwellen) facies. This crustal instability announced the approach of the Bretonian orogeny. At the end of the Devonian the southern and central Schiefergebirge were intensely folded for the first time.

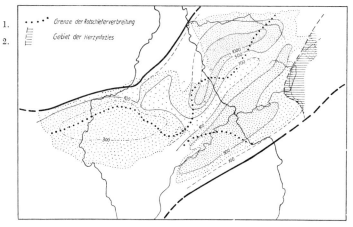

1. Limit of distribution of red shales.
2. Area of the Hercyn facies.

Fig. 13. The Rhenish-Ardennes geosyncline in the Upper Emsian stage. Thickness of sediment, redbed facies from the northern and southern coasts toward the basin and distribution of the Hercyn facies are shown (after W. Kegel and W. Schmidt)

Harz. The facies- and tectonic zones of the Rhenish uplands continued in the strike of the geosyncline and are further revealed in the Harz. The Harz may be correspondingly divided into two parts, each of which shows a different structure. The northwestern part, the Oberharz, is characterized by its Rhenish Devonian facies. The Unterharz, SE of Brocken, by the occurrence of the Hercyn (which takes its name from here) corresponds with the eastern margin of the Schiefergebirge.

In the Oberharz neither the oldest Devonian nor the pre-Devonian base comes to the surface. The exposed strata begin with the Upper Emsian in a typical Rhenish development and lead to the Wissenbach beds and to the diabase and schalstein of the Oberharz greenstone tract, in which once again hematitic iron ore occurs. The Upper Devonian shows its usual characteristics.

The basement of the Unterharz, which was folded in the Caledonian orogeny, was dry land at the beginning of the Devonian. It was first covered over by moderately thick strata with Hercyn fauna in the late Lower Devonian. The higher Middle Devonian, as in the Oberharz, was marked by basic volcanic activity. In the Upper Devonian of the Unterharz is a premature incidence of the Kulm facies (p. 46), which is characteristic of the Lower Carboniferous. The Tanne trough became filled with gray-wacke derived from the Central German axis.

The *Franconian-Thuringian Schiefergebirge* belonged to the uplift area of the Kellerwald-Unterharz and reveal a thin Lower Devonian or even the lack of it. The beginning of the Upper Devonian was a time of lively volcanic and tectonic activity. Diabase and schalstein interfinger with lenses of reef limestones, bedded limestones and hematitic ironstone deposits.

East Germany and Poland. The keel of the Variscan geosyncline, which extends from the Rhenish Schiefergebirge to the Oberharz, bends toward the SE at the Elbe River. In the northern part of the Svientokrzyz Hills of central Poland the Ludlow passes without a break into the Devonian. From this marine area, east Sudetia was flooded in the Siegenian stage, the Elbe valley zone, Jeschken Mountains and Moravia in the Middle Devonian, and west Sudetia, which had been folded in the Caledonian orogeny, in the Upper Devonian. The Devonian of east Sudetia is mostly clastic. Here, too, occurs the previously mentioned association of schalstein, limestone, and ironstone. In west Sudetia and near Brno the Upper Devonian consists partly of cephalopod-bearing nodular limestones and partly of thick graywackes. Beginning with the Adorf and Nehden stages, it rests unconformably on the pre-Devonian basis.

In the region of the *Upper Rhine,* a parallel widening of the Variscan geosynclinal region took place during the course of the Devonian. The southern coast of the Schiefergebirge trough must have lain a little south of the Hunsrück and Taunus in the Lower Devonian. The Middle Devonian sea reached the Upper Rhine Massifs, and the Upper Devonian sea, the northern part of the Central Massif of France (the Morvan). The Middle Devonian of the Vosges (Breusch valley, Belfort) is composed of unmistakable near-shore, conglomeratic deposits; shales predominate in the higher Upper Devonian.

Bohemia. The transgression over the outer margin of the Bohemian Massif was balanced in the inner part of the Massif by a gradual retreat of the sea which by the end of the Middle Devonian had become complete. In the beginning of the Lower Devonian the deposition of fossiliferous reef limestone and bedded limestone continued. Then, however, reef growth stopped. Nodular limestone and marls followed, which in the highest

Middle Devonian were finally replaced by shales and graywackes that resemble flysch.

Southern Europe. The Bohemian bay opened toward the S into the south European Devonian sea, whose other shore is to be found in North Africa. The Devonian of the eastern Alps stands close to the Bohemian in facies and fauna. In the Carnic Alps and near Graz, the mountain peaks consist of reef limestones, which reach up to 1000 m. thick, and which overlie the Silurian conformably. Almost the entire Devonian system is here represented by reef limestones. Limestones of the same age in the graywacke zone have been later transformed metasomatically into valuable siderite ore deposits (for example Erzberg in Styria). In the Montagne Noire and in the eastern Pyrenees, the Devonian is similarly composed predominantly of limestone. Instances which lie further S — in Asturia, the Spanish Meseta, Dobrudsha, Bosphorus, Asia Minor, Morocco, and in the North African desert table-land — are on the other hand, more closely related to the Rhenish development.

British Isles. W of the Ardennes the northern border of the Variscan geosyncline appears again in southwest England and may be followed into southern Eire. In Cornwall and Devonshire, strata containing a Rhenish fauna are interbedded with red sandstone that includes plant and fish remains. The continental facies prevails more and more toward the NE; the furthermost outlier of marine Devonian reaches South Wales.

North of this coastal fringe lay the Old Red continent. At the beginning of the Devonian the mobility of the crust and the magmatic activity in the region of the earlier Caledonian trough had by no means been extinguished. The older parts of the Old Red period were therefore still restless. Continental basins which followed the strike of the mountains were formed; in these up to 6000 m. of sediment accumulated. Two unconformities divide the deposits. After the older, more intense orogenesis granite and granodiorite, with here and there alkalic syenite also, were emplaced in Scotland and in the north of England as an aftermath of the Caledonian intrusion phase.

Widespread, chiefly andesitic volcanics are connected with these rocks. The eruptions first ceased in the Upper Old Red. The sediments of the Old Red consist of conglomerates, red, commonly friable arkoses and sandstones, variegated silts and clays. Cross-stratification, ripples, mud-cracks, and sparse fossil content are to be found — in short, all signs of a fluvial-lacustrine origin in a semi-arid climate. In the Upper Old Red the sandstones are generally lighter-colored and purer. Ventifacts and calcareous and siliceous crusts testify to more arid conditions of deposition. Plants, eurypterids, and armored fish comprise almost the only fossils of the Old Red. The latter are found chiefly in bedded calcareous sandstones or bituminous marls, which may have originated in lagoons.

Northern and eastern Europe. In contrast to the British Isles the Caledonian Mountains in the Scandinavian lands remained an area of uplift and at the same time elevated the Swedish-Finnish foreland. In this way Fennoscandia originated; it has continued to rise even to the present time.

Devon des Old Red-Festlandes

Abteilungen u.Stufen	Leitende Agna-then u.Fische	Schottland	Mittelengland und Wales	Russische Tafel (Ostbaltikum)	Nordfrankreich (Artois)
Hangendes:		Unterkarbon (Calciferous Sandstone)	Carboniferous Lower Limestone	Tscherny-schino	Oberkreide
Ober-Devon VI / III-V / II / I	Groenlandaspis / Remigolepis / Phyllolepis / Psammosteus (Bothriolepis, Holoptychius)	500-1000m Oberes Old.Red Nairn / Rosebrae ?	Lower Carbo-niferous 100 m Lower Limestone shales / 200 m Oberes Old Red (Farlovian)	Unter-karbon Upa / Malevko-Muraevna / 120m Oberes Old Red / 100m Dolomit-St.	
Mittel-Devon Ob. / Unt.	Laccognathus / Heterostius (Asterolepis)	Old.Red Caithness + + + + + +		200m Unteres Old Red	
Unter-Devon Ems / Siegen / Ob. / Gedinne / Unt.	Pteraspis dunensis / Pter. leachi / Pter. crouchi, rostrata / Pter. leathensis / Traquair-aspis / Hemi-cyclaspis Thyestes Sclerodus (Didymaspis, Cephalaspis)	1000-5000m Unteres Old Red (Caledonian) / 900m Downton	Breconian 1000-2000m Unteres Old Red / Dittonian / 600m Ledbury group Downton: Temeside gr. Downton Castle gr. Ludlow Bone Bed		200m Sandstein v.Vimy / 20m Sdst.v.Pernes / 70m Sdst.v.Liévin / 20m, Schf.v.Méricourt
Liegendes:		Ludlow / Ordoviz	Oberludlow (Whitcliffe flags) / Mittelludlow (Aymestry group)	Ob.Gotlandium (Öselsch.)	20m Grw.v.Drocourt / 50m Kalk v.Angres / 15m Kalk v.Liévin

Debris eroded from this source covered the east European platform with the partly continental, partly shallow marine deposits of the east Baltic-Russian Old Red. The eastern and southern border areas of the crystalline platform, toward the Ural and Caucasian geosynclines, were covered from the lowest Devonian onward. In the central area the Old Red sets in with the upper Middle Devonian and consists of non-marine red sandstones and clays, into which are intercalated in the lower Upper Devonian marine dolomites and in the higher Upper Devonian salt deposits.

Arctic. The Old Red continent extends to the Arctic on the N. More than 1000 m. of variegated sandstones with the same fauna and flora as in Europe have been identified on Spitzbergen and in east Greenland. The

Marines Devon

Stratigraphische Korrelationstabelle des marinen Devons.

Abteilung	Stufe	Leitfossilien	Ardennen	Eifel-Hohes Venn	Bergisches Land	Siegerland-Sauerland / Mittelrhein	Lahngebiet-Taunus	Giessen-Kellerwald	Oberharz	Unterharz	Thüring. Schiefergeb.	Sudeten Ost	Sudeten West	Böhmen	Ostalpen Karn.A.,Graz	Nordamerika
	Hängendes:	Gattendorfia	Unterkarbon (Sch. v. Maredsous)	Trias (Buntsandstein)	Unterkarbon (Hangenbergkalk)	Unterkarbon (Kulmkieselschiefer)	(Kellerwaldquarzit)	Unterkarbon (Gattend. sch)	(Alaunschiefer)	Oberkarbon / 800m Tanner Grauw.	Unterkarbon (Gattendorfiakalk)	(Kulm) (Gattend. k.)	Oberkarbon	Unterkarbon (Kulm)	Mississippian (Kinderhook)
Oberdevon	Dasbergstufe	VI Wocklumeria-Kalloclymenia u. Hastière; V Oxyclymenia Gonioclymenia	Psammites de Condroz	150m Etrœungtsch. Sch.v.Etrœungt.; Strunien; Famennien	10m Hangenbergkalk; 5m Schiefer; 150m Dasbergsch.; 700m Velberter Sch.; Pönsandstein 50m Hembergschiefer	5m Wocklumer Kalk; 40m Graue; 50m Rote; 10m Grünl. (Graugrüne)	150m Obere (Graue); 50m Mittlere (Rote); 50m Untere	15m Cephalopodenknollenkalk (Clymenienkalk, Kramenzelkalk)	Hundshäuser Grauwacke u. Urfer Sch.; 150m Bunt- u. Kieselschf.	50m Cypridinenschiefer	15m Clymenienkalk; 100m Ortberggrauw.	600m Selke- u. Südharzgrauw.; 100m Buntschiefer	200m Cypridinenschiefer	30m Cephalopodenknollenkalk; Oberdevonkalk	Oberdevon	130m Bradfor-Oswayo dian Conewango; Chautau-quan Cassadaga	Chattanooga
	Hembergstufe	IV Platyclymenia; III Prolobites		Famenne Sdst.			Cypridinenschiefer (fossley)				Quarzitschf.			Steinbergkalk		
	Nehdenstufe	II Cheiloceras	Schiefer v. famenne	400m Kalkknoten Schf.	200m Nehdener Sdst.; 50m Nehdener Schf.	5m Knollenkalke (Kramenzelkalke)		150m Bunt- u. Kieselschf.	50m Ortberggrauw.						
	Adorfstufe	I Manticoceras δ (β) γ α	Schiefer v. Matagne; Schf. v. Frasnes; Schiefer v. Fromelennes	50m Büdesheimer Sch.; 30m Ooser Plattenkalk; 30m Wallersheimer Dol.	150m Matagneschiefer; 100m Iberger Kalk; 250m Dorper Kalk	Flinzkalk u.-schiefer	10m Adorfer Kalk; 5m Roteisenstein (Grenzlager)	50m Buchenauer Schichten; 15m Adorfer Kalk; ~150m Iberger Kalk	1m Kellwasserkalk; Bänderschf. u. Kieselschf.	50m Büdesheimer Schiefer; 10m Adorfer Kalk	½m Kellwasserkalk; 75m Iberger Kalk	100m Kieselschiefer; 100m Planschwitzer Tuff	5m Adorfer K.	Engelsberger Sch.	Bunte Flaserkalke	Chemung; Seneca; Naples; Genesee
Mitteldevon	Givetstufe (Stringocephalen)	Maenioceras	Kalk v. Givet	100m Eifeldolomit; 30m Kerpener Sch.; 50m Rodert-Sch.; 30m Dreimühlen-Sch.; 250m Fleringer Schichten	500m Massenkalk; 1000m Honseler Schichten	3m Roteisenstein; 40m Hauptgrünstein; Ob. 600m Finnentroper Sch., Tentaculitenschiefer u. Bänderschiefer	500m Diabas, Schalstein, Keratophyr u. Roteisenstein (Schalsteinlager)	500m Massenkalk (Stringo-cephalenkalk); Tentaculitenschiefer	Discoideskalk; 50m Stringocephalenkalk u. Flinz	200m Schalstein, Diabas u. Roteisenstein; Odershäuser Kalk; 40m Calceolaschiefer	300m Stieger Sch.; 200m Hauptquarzit; 30m Hasselfelder K.	50m Schwärzschiefer; insges. ca 2000m Schalstein v. Sternberg-Bennisch; Tentaculiten-knollenkalk	Ton-schiefer	Sch. v. Roblín; 150m Hochlanisch.; Sch. v. Srbsko Kačák	300m Taghanic Tully; Tioughnioga Hamilton; Cazenovia; Marcellus
	Eifelstufe (Couvin-Calceola-)	Anarcestes	Schichten v. Couvin; Schichten v. Bure	100m Rommersheimer Sch.; 50m Ahrdorfer Schichten; 75m Nohner Sch.; 40m Laucher Sch.	600m Brandenbergschichten; 250m Mühlenbergschichten; 500m Hobräcker Sch.	500m Selscheider Schichten; Mühlenbergsch.; 100m Stöppeler Schf.	300m Tentaculiten- (Stylialinen-) schiefer	500m Wissenbacher (Orthoceras-) Schiefer	Güntegröder Kalk; Ballersbacher Kalk	500m Wissenbacher (Goslarer) Schiefer	200m			50m K.v. Chotec; 50m Sch.v. Třebotov u. Daleje	250m Barrandei-kalk; 600m Dol.-Sdst.-Sch.; 5m Krinoiden-K.	Cazenovia; Marcellus
Unterdevon	Ems- (Koblenz-) stufe Ob./Unt.	Spirifer cultrijugatus; Spirifer paradoxus; Spirifer pellico; Spirifer arduennensis	Sch. v. Hierges; Sch. v. Winenne; Sch. v. Vireux	200m Oberems; Wiltzer Sch.; Emsquarzit; 1500m Unterems; Stadtfelder Schichten	300m Cultrijugatuszone; 200m Hohenhofer Sch.; ~600m Remscheider Sch.; 220m Rimmertquarzit; 500m Bensberger Sch.; Wahnbachsch.	500m Oberemssch.; 100m Emsquarzit; 1000m Unteremssch.; Nellenköpfchensch.; Vallendarer Sch.; Singhofener Sch.; Spitznack Sch.	500m Oberems; 100m Michelbacher Schichten; 3m Dalmanitensch.; 4m Schönauer Kalk; 5m K.m.Rh. princeps	Kondelsch., Laubacher Sch., Höhenrheiner Sch., Emsquarzit; 2000m	500m Kahlebergsandstein	30m Mittl. Herzyn-K.; 10m Kalkgeröllgrauw.; 8m Dalmanitensch.; 5m Lauterberger (Zorgensis-)K.; 10m K.m.Rh. princeps; 10m Rothäuser Kalkgrauw.		Würbenthaler Sch.	Kalk v. Zlichov; Kalk v. Braník; K.v. Řeporyje-Lodenice	30m Sandstein	Onondaga; Onesquethaw; Schoharie; Esopus; Oriskany; Deerpark
	Siegenstufe Ob./Mittl./Unt.	Spirifer primaevus	Grauw. de Grupont; Grauw. de Petigny; Grauw. de St. Michel; Grés d'Anor; Schf. v. St. Hubert	2000m Siegener Sch.; Rurberger Sch.; Monschauer Sch.	500m Siegener Sch.	Ulmensch.; Herdorfer Sch.; Rauhflaserhorizont; Tonschieferhorizont; Hermeskeilschichten	Hunsrückschiefer; 500m Taunusquarzit; 10m Erbslochgrauw.	3000m		25m Tentaculiten-knollenkalk			Kalk v. Slivenec; Ob. Konĕprusy-K.; K.v. Vinařice	1000m Sandstein	Ulstequethaw
	Gedinnestufe Ob./Unt.	Spirifer dumontianus; Spirifer elevatus (mercuri)	Bunte Schiefer v. Oignies; Sch. v. Mondrepuits; Kongl. v. Fepin	400m Bunte Schiefer; 10m Arkose v. Weismes-Gdoumont	600m Bunte Ebbesch.; 700m Bredeneck-Sch.; 300m Hüinghäuser Sch.	800m Bunte Ebbesch.; 500m ? Silberger Schiefer	200m Bunte Phyllite; Graue Phyllite	250m Kieselgallenschiefer; m. Sowerbyella minor; m. Sow. mariae					Kalk v. Braník	200m Riffkalke	Deerpark; Helderberg
	Liegendes:	Monograptus		Kambrium u. Silur	Silur (Köbbinghäuser Sch.)				Silur (Harzgeröder Kalk)		Silur (Ob. Grapt.Schf.)	Krist.-Silur	Silur (Sch. v. Lochkov)	Silur	Helderberg

most important discoveries are remains of the oldest amphibians. Here, too, the overlapping higher Old Red covers greater areas than do the deposits of the lower stages.

General Features

Climate and environment. Widespread continental deposits occur in the Devonian for the first time in the course of Earth history precisely at the same time as the animals and plants proceeded to the conquest of the continental living spaces. At first they lived in basins of fresh or brackish-water and their surroundings. An unbroken plant cover, which would hinder erosion and transport as in later periods, was, however, still lacking. Therefore, one may consider the poorly fossiliferous, brightly colored Old Red not directly a desert deposit.

The climate apparently got gradually warmer. The clastic, low carbonate Lower Devonian sediments composing the Rhenish facies suggests the sea had been cooler. With the transition to Middle Devonian these sediments were widely replaced by coral reef limestones. Finally evaporites, such as anhydrite and rock salt, are limited almost entirely to the higher Upper Devonian.

Crustal movements and magmatism. The Caledonian orogeny forms a sharp boundary between the Silurian and Devonian, particularly in central- and northern Europe. In the N, as a result of folding of the Caledonian geosyncline, the Hebrides mass, Greenland, and the Baltic-Russian Shield grew together to form the Old Red continent. This block became the northern frame of the Variscan geosyncline, which now appeared as a quickly subsiding trough, particularly in the Devonian and Lower Carboniferous. Taken as a whole, the Devonian transgression reached its peak in the later stages, though the movements of the sea did not follow any general rule.

Lower Carboniferous
～～～～～～～Bretonian phase of folding (southern Rhenish Schiefergebirge)

Upper Devonian   Transgression (Variscan geosyncline; Russian platform)

Regression (Bohemia)

Middle Devonian   Transgression (Ruhr area; Ardennes; upper Rhine area)

Lower Devonian   Transgression (Variscan geosyncline)

～～～～～～～Ardennes phase of folding (Caledonian Mountains, Ardennes, Sudetia)

Ludlow

Plate 4. Devonian index fossils

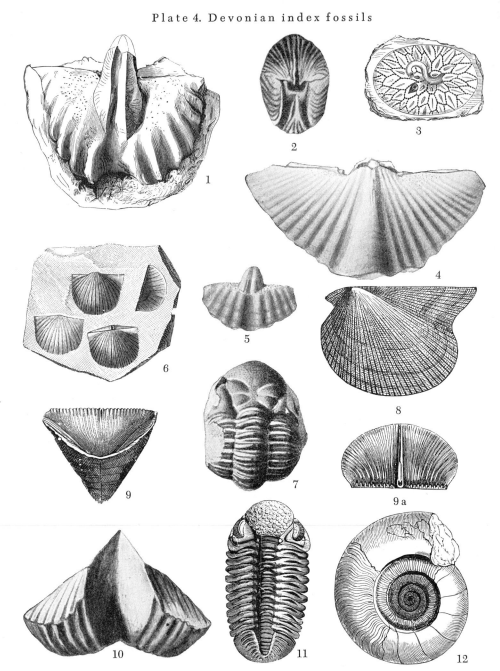

Siegenian: 1. *Spirifer (Acrospirifer) primaevus* STEINING. 2 *Rhenorensselaeria crassicosta* C. KOCH. Emsian: 3. *Pleurodictyum problematicum* GOLDF. 4. *Spirifer (Acrospirifer) paradoxus* SCHLOTH. 5. *Spirifer (Acrospirifer) arduennensis* SCHNUR. 6. *Chonetes plebeja* SCHNUR. 7. *Asteropyge kochi* KAYS. 8. *Pterinea lineata* GOLDF. Eifelian: 9, 9a. *Calceola sandalina* LAM. 10. *Spirifer (Paraspirifer) cultrijugatus* F. ROEM. 11. *Phacops schlotheimi* BRONN. 12. *Anarcestes lateseptatus* BEYR.

Plate 5. Devonian index fossils

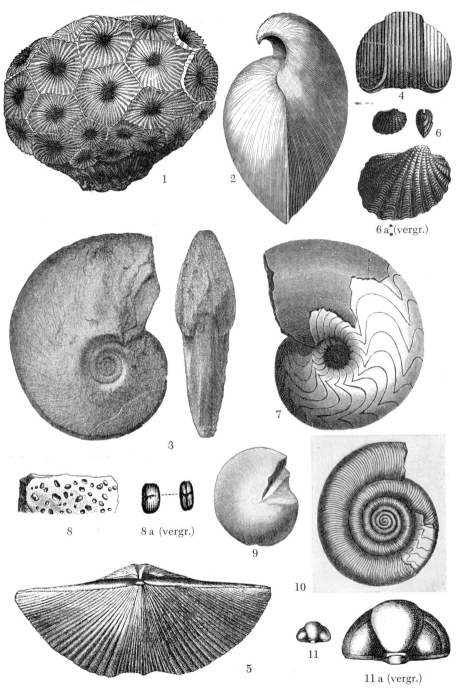

Givetian: 1. *Hexagonaria hexagonum* GOLDF. 2. *Stringocephalus burtini* DEFR. 3. *Agoniatites inconstans* PHILL. Upper Devonian I: 4. *Hypothyridina cuboides* SOW. 5. *Spirifer (Cyrtospirifer) verneuili* MURCH. 6, 6 a. *Buchiola retrostriata* v. BUCH. 7. *Manticoceras intumescens* BEYR. Upper Devonian II: 8, 8 a. *Entomis serratostriata* SANDB. 9. *Cheiloceras subpartitum* v. MÜNST. Upper Devonian V/VI: 10. *Kosmoclymenia undulata* v. MÜNST. 11, 11 a. *Trimerocephalus anophthalmus* FRECH.

Volcanoes extruded predominantly diabasic-keratophyric lavas; they were especially active in the Variscan geosyncline during the Middle Devonian.

Retrospect. The preparatory geosynclinal time of the Variscan mountains began with the Devonian. In the course of this period the newly formed trough widened and deepened, and it was accompanied by the production of basic lavas.

The widespread uplift of the land, which followed the Caledonian folding in northern Europe and the Arctic, was paralleled by changes in the organic world. Tetrapods developed from the Devonian armored fish. The first vascular plants emerged from the sea and proceeded simultaneously with the animals to the conquest of dry land.

Supplementary Articles

E. Asselberghs: L'Eodévonien de l'Ardenne. Mém. Inst. Géol. Louvain 14. 1946.

G. Bischoff and W. Ziegler: Die Conodontenchronologie des Mitteldevons und des tiefsten Oberdevons. Abh. Hess. L.-Amt Bodenforsch. 22. 1957.

H. Ehrenberg u. a.: Das Schwefelkies-Zinkblende-Schwerspatlager von Meggen (Westfalen). Beih. Geol. Jb. 12. 1954.

W. Gross: Die Bedeutung der Wirbeltierfauna des Oldreds und des marinen Paläozoikums. Abh. Dtsch. Ak. Wiss. Math.-nat. Kl. 1950.

W. Kegel: Sedimentation und Tektonik in der rheinischen Geosynklinale. Z. Dtsch. Geol. Ges. 100, 267. 1950.

K. Krömmelbein u. a.: Zur Geologie der Eifelkalkmulden. Beih. Geol. Jb. 17. 1955.

A. Rabien: Zur Taxionomie und Chronologie der Oberdevonischen Ostracoden. Abh. Hess. L.-Amt Bodenforsch. 9. 1954.

R. Richter: Tierwelt und Umwelt im Hunsrückschiefer. Senckenbergiana 13, 299. 1931. 17, 244. 1935. 18, 215. 1936.

R. & E. Richter: Die Trilobiten des Ebbe-Sattels. Abh. Senckenb. Naturf. Ges. 488. 1954.

W. Schmidt: Die paläogeographische Entwicklung des linksrheinischen Schiefergebirges. Z. Dtsch. Geol. Ges. 103, 151. 1952.

G. Solle: Die Spiriferen der Gruppe arduennensis—intermedius im rheinischen Devon. Abh. Hess. L.-Amt Bodenforsch. 5. 1953.

Chapter 7.

Carboniferous

Preliminary Remarks

Boundaries and classification. The Carboniferous, the system of the Coal Measures, is easily identified and therefore very early established as a stratigraphical type. In 1808, J. B. Omalius d'Halloy introduced the term "terrain houiller" and distinguished the Carboniferous limestone from the overlying productive coal measures. The further subdivision, as the names of the different stages reveal, are connected in part with Belgian conditions. About 1850, L. de Koninck described the rich fauna of the Carboniferous limestone from Belgium nearly simultaneously with McCoy in Ireland and J. Phillips in England. Study of the Upper Carboniferous depends on knowledge of fossil flora, for which we are indebted to E. F. von Schlotheim, K. v. Sternberg, A. Brongniart, H. Goeppert.

More recently research into the Carboniferous has been undertaken especially by F. Frech, H. Potonié, W. Gothan, H. Schmidt, and O. H. Schindewolf in Germany; by W. Jongmans in Holland; G. Delépine, A. Renier, and F. Demanet in Belgium; B. Renault, R. Zeiller, and P. Pruvost in France; W. Hind, A. Vaughan, R. G. Carruthers, D. H. Scott, R. Kidston, A. E. Trueman, T. N. George, and W. Bisat in England, and H. Trautschold, Th. Tchernishev, and M. Zalessky in Russia.

The lower boundary of the Carboniferous is marked by the sudden evolution of the plant world. Plant remains, which were sparse in the Devonian, now became widespread, and for the first time in the course of Earth history accumulated in large quantities as coal seams. The system lacks a clear natural upper limit; this boundary is drawn by agreement.

The **distribution** of the Carboniferous is very well known, thanks to the great practical value of its coal-bearing stages. The Lower Carboniferous follows the pattern of the Devonian. Afterwards, however, mountain-building pushed the sea back in many places. In central Europe, the Variscan geosyncline was constricted to a narrow land-bound channel from which the sea was gradually retreating; this is marked by the line of the coal-mining-districts of northern France, Belgium, the Ruhr area, and Upper Silesia. Continental coal-basins originated in the uplifted parts of the mountains. Similar events took place in other Variscan fold-zones in south Europe and elsewhere. Coal was formed also on some of the older massives, e.g. the areas of the British Isles consolidated by the Caledonian orogeny, and on the Russian platform.

Principal Regions (Fig. 14—17)

In **central and western Europe the Lower Carboniferous** embraces the interval between two of the chief phases of the Variscan fold-era. The Bretonian orogeny occurred at the beginning of the Carboniferous and folded part of the southern border of the Variscan geosyncline. During the Lower Carboniferous the marginal depression along the northwestern border of the Central German axis (Fig. 15 a) continued to move outward. Débris from the axis filled the depression — in the Upper Devonian the Tanne graywacke (p. 38), in the oldest Lower Carboniferous the pale Kamm quartzite of the Hörre-Acker tract which extends from Giessen trough the Kellerwald and central Harz to Magdeburg. Fine-grained sediments were deposited seaward from the coastal region. These were principally lydite and siliceous shale, which one must consider as eupelagic sediments in spite of their association here and there with graywackes. At that time, therefore, the Variscan geosyncline underwent a deep-sea phase, comparable with that in progress today in parts of the Indonesian archipelago. The approach of a new episode of mountain-building was heralded toward the end of the Lower Carboniferous. After some preliminary orogenic phases which gripped the southern border of the trough, the Central German crystalline axis was raised anew. Thick graywackes and conglomerates pushed forward widely into the shallowing basin. With the transition to the Upper Carboniferous the entire geosyncline was heaved up and folded during the Sudetian orogeny into the Variscan Mountains (p. 49). Only a narrow strip along the northern coast remained untouched.

Geosynclinal volcanism, after its first climax during the Middle Devonian (p. 36), attained its second and last maximum in the mid-Lower Carboniferous. Basic lavas were again produced, which can be distinguished from those of the Devonian only by their smaller gas content and more Pacific chemical composition. The principal eruptions followed at the beginning of the deep-sea phase and took place mainly on the slopes between the Central German axis and the deeply subsiding basin north of it. A sudden change to silicic magmatic types occurred in the Viséan. Porphyric lavas were discharged in conjunction with young lower Carboniferous granitic intrusives in the zone from the Central Massif of France to the Upper Rhine. In weaker eruptions these reached central Germany and may here be interpreted as forerunners of the granitic melts, which filled extensive plutons in the Sudetian phase.

Ardennes and Rhenish Schiefergebirge. In Belgium and near Aachen the Lower Carboniferous is developed as Carboniferous limestone, as in northwest Europe. The arrangement of the facies (Fig. 14) indicates that the deposits, which attain a thickness of 700 m. and are fossiliferous throughout, originated in a broad sea channel that fringed the Brabant Massif on the S. East of the Rhine, near Düsseldorf, the Carboniferous limestone interfingers with the Kulm complex of graywackes, shales, lydites and bedded limestones which prevails in the remainder of the German Lower Carboniferous. The Kellerwald lay especially near the Central German axis. The older Lower Carboniferous is developed here as the Kellerwald quartzite. Conglomeratic graywackes occur in the younger Kulm. As one goes further N, the graywacke sediments begin later and are finer grained; thus on the northern edge of the Schiefergebirge the Kulm is quite free of graywacke. The Lahn and Dill synclines belong to the volcanic zone along the northern slope of the Central German axis. Eruptions reached a peak here with the thick effusives known as the Deck diabase.

In the *Harz*, as in the Devonian (p. 37), the facies zones of the Lahn-Dill area and the eastern Schiefergebirge are again exposed, the former in the Oberharz, the latter in the Unterharz. The movement of the marginal depression toward the NW may be observed here, too. The filling of the Upper Devonian trough by the Tanne graywacke of the Unterharz was followed in the oldest Lower Carboniferous by the Bruchberg-Acker

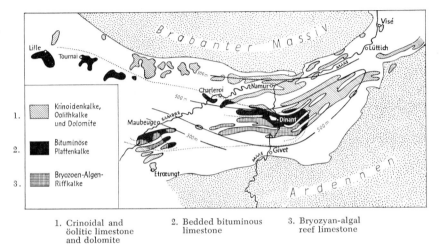

1. Crinoidal and öolitic limestone and dolomite

2. Bedded bituminous limestone

3. Bryozyan-algal reef limestone

Fig. 14. Facies and thickness of the Carboniferous limestone in the Belgian-French coal regions. Dotted: pre-Devonian and Lower Devonian. White: younger Devonian and Upper Carboniferous (after G. Delépine)

quartzite and in the latest Lower Carboniferous by the Kulm graywacke of the Oberharz.

The trough south of the Central German axis, to which in the Lower Carboniferous *Saxony* and the *Franconian-Thuringian Schiefergebirge* belonged, did not sink so deeply as did the northern basin. Lydite and diabase therefore are nearly or completely lacking.

The *Black Forest, Vosges* and *Central Massif* of France lay on the north-west border of the Alemannic-Bohemian island, which had divided the central European geosyncline from the south European basin since the earlier Paleozoic. These massifs developed faster than the Variscan as a whole, in that the principal folding and intrusion took place in the younger Lower Carboniferous. Gattendorfia beds underlie the unconformity in the Black Forest; conglomerate with a late Lower Carboniferous flora rests above this. The mountain-building was accompanied by the ascent of granitic magma and the effusion of porphyries and porphyrites.

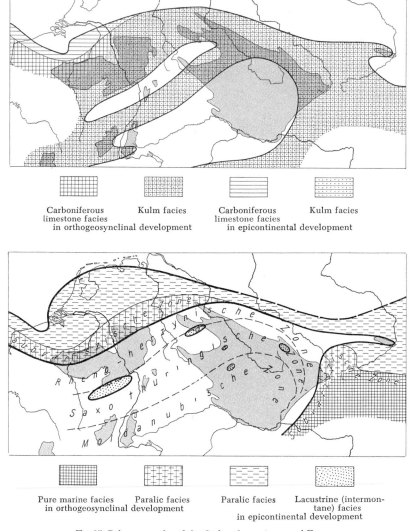

Carboniferous   Kulm facies   Carboniferous   Kulm facies
limestone facies   limestone facies
    in orthogeosynclinal development   in epicontinental development

Pure marine facies   Paralic facies   Paralic facies   Lacustrine (intermon-
    in orthogeosynclinal development   tane) facies
                                                in epicontinental development

Fig. 15. Paleogeography of the Carboniferous in central Europe

Above: Higher Lower Carboniferous
Below: Middle Upper Carboniferous (with the zones of the Variscan Mountains)

In the Vosges and in Morvan, the northern spur of the Central Massif,
fossiliferous Lower Carboniferous is also known.

Sudetia. As in the Devonian, eastern Sudetia was a region of great subsidence in the Lower Carboniferous and therefore contrasts with western
Sudetia, which has a moderately thick sediment cover owing to its con-

solidation in the Caledonian orogeny. The Silesian-Moravian slate-gray-
wacke formation includes several 1000 m. of marine beds which pass
upward conformably into the Upper Carboniferous of the Upper Silesian
basin. Western Sudetia, on the other hand, experienced only a short-
lived transgression which was derived from the east Sudetian sea.

Upper Carboniferous in central and western Europe. The Variscan
mountains were formed principally in the Sudetian phase.

A fold tract more than 500 km. wide but gradually narrowing and with
northeasterly strike crossed from Brittany and the Central Massif to west-
and central Germany. At the line of the Elbe the already much diminished
chain bends toward the SE and its branches can be followed in Silesia,
Moravia, and central Poland. Outward from within, that is, from S to N,
the following zones can be distinguished:

1. The Moldanubian zone consists of crystalline rocks which outcrop in
   the French Central Massif, the Upper Rhine Massifs and the Bohemian
   Massif. Non-metamorphosed sediments form only a moderately thick
   and incomplete cover. Block faults and extensive intrusions predominate over true folds.

2. The Saxo-Thuringian zone. The crystalline basement is exposed here
   only in a few domes. The effects of Caledonian movements are
   widely distributed. After the intense subsidence in the Cambro-
   Silurian, the region underwent in the Devonian and Lower Carboniferous only an occasional inundation. Folding was limited to the
   regions of subsidence that had been filled by thick sedimentary accu-
   mulations, which were overthrust by the margins of the rigidified
   older nuclei.

3. The Rheno-Hercynian zone followed the keel of the Variscan geosyncline and is distinguished by a thick Devonian-Kulm sequence.
   This region, almost without disturbance from older massifs, was
   thrown into free folds overturned toward the NW or NE. Intrusions
   are far scarcer than in the inner zones.

4. The zone of the sub-Variscan foredeep extended beyond the outer
   margin of the mountains. It was connected to the northern margin of
   the Variscan chain by the Upper Carboniferous orogeny.

Lively epeirogenic crustal warping in both the mountain regions and the
foredeep, made the Upper Carboniferous unique. In the mountains, continental basins, which were elongated in strike and bordered by uplifted
areas, originated; in the course of time these increased in number, expanded, and widened (Fig. 15, 18). This development, which continued
until the end of the Lower Permian, was only slightly influenced by the

orogenic movements in the higher Upper Carboniferous and Middle Rotliegend.

The sub-Variscan foredeep is the most important of the Carboniferous
troughs, in view of its linear extent and its filling of more than 6000 m.
thick. True, this sedimentary column does not occur in any single section.
The principal axis of subsidence and therefore the zone of greatest
thickness shifted from within outwards. This movement, which had already
begun in the Lower Carboniferous, was continued. At the end of the
Westphalian stage the Asturian orogeny ended the development of the
foredeep and attached it to the Variscan Mountains. The folding died out
gradually toward the northern regions. The Upper Carboniferous of the
foreland is today still horizontal.

Interior and marginal areas of subsidence can be recognized by their
relation to the sea. The paralic facies of the foredeep with its numerous
marine ingressions contrasts with the lacustrine or intermontane deposits
of the continental basins. The fillings of both kinds of basins are petrographically similar. Conglomerates, arkoses, and shales predominate. Coal-
seams from a few decimeters to a few meters thick, seldom form more
than 2—3 percent of the whole. The seams originated in the depressions
of alluvial plains. Swampy forest transected by areas of open water
flourished here until flooding or burial ended their growth. This recurred
many times, as the cyclic structure of the succession shows. Some investigators have explained this phenomenon by tectonic subsidence which proceeded sometimes slowly, at other times quickly. Others attribute them
to eustatic changes of level or to periodic shifting of deltas. In general the
coal is richest in the lower Westphalian. It decreases in the Upper Westphalian, and in many places the Stephanian has no coal seams. The transition upward in the accompanying deposits from grey to red suggests
increasing aridity.

In place of the basic rocks of the geosynclinal period Pacific silicic
melts were brought up by the magma movements of the Upper Carboniferous. Granite and quartz porphyry predominate. Plutonic activity reached
a first climax in the Sudetian phase and a second, less significant, in the
Asturian phase. Cooling of the masses followed; the majority of the vein
deposits in the central German uplands belong to the later Upper Carboniferous and older Permian. Volcanic activity continued throughout the
Upper Carboniferous and reached a new peak in the Lower Permian; the
chief theater was the Saxo-Thuringian zone.

Northern France, Belgium, and Holland. Boulogne, Lens, Douai, Namur,
and Liège mark the line of the foredeep, whose depth increased toward
the E. The Upper Carboniferous reaches 2000 m. thick in Northern France,
3000 m. in Belgium. The folded Carboniferous of the marginal deep near

Liège and Maastricht adjoins the horizontal foreland Carboniferous of southern Holland and northern Belgium, which faulting had broken into single blocks (Peel, Campine).

Aachen, Lower Rhine, and Westphalia. The Ruhr is the most important area for coal in central Europe. Its reserves amount to more than 40 billion tons down to 1200 m. depth. The productive coal measures are exposed only in the Ruhr and near Aachen and Osnabrück, but are known to underlie the later strata from Amsterdam to Hannover. The structural position of the beds permits demonstration of a zone of subsidence which migrated northward and gradually became shallower and finally dry land. The lower Namurian, the Flözleere, is throughout the foredeep of marine origin. During the Upper Carboniferous the facies of the productive coal measures moved from the S into this area and pushed the open sea back. Coal correspondingly begins to form in the later strata toward the N. At the same time, ingressions of the sea became less common. Instead, in Westphalian D, red coal-free sandstones appear. The clastic sediments of the older Upper Carboniferous originated chiefly in the Rhenish Schiefergebirge and the Central German axis. In the later Upper Carboniferous, however, they came principally from the northern continent which had been folded in the Caledonian era (p. 28). The Asturian orogeny, with its forerunner which had begun in the Westphalian, folded a strip about 60 km wide adjoining the Schiefergebirge; the intensity of folding decreased toward the N.

In *Upper Silesia,* the Carboniferous, which had disappeared in eastern Westphalia under an ever-thickening cover, is again exposed. It is, however, doubtful whether both districts are joined by a continuous coal belt under the north German plain. The foredeep narrowed sharply if not vanished to the east of the Ruhr, but widened anew in the bay formed by eastern

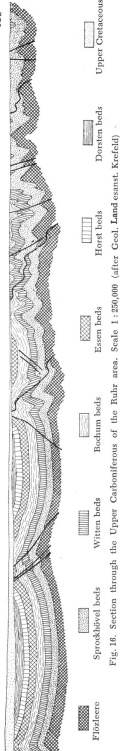

Fig. 16. Section through the Upper Carboniferous of the Ruhr area. Scale 1 : 250,000 (after Geol. Landesanst. Krefeld)

Flözleere

Sprockhövel beds

Witten beds

Bochum beds

Essen beds

Horst beds

Dorsten beds

Upper Cretaceous

SSE

NNW

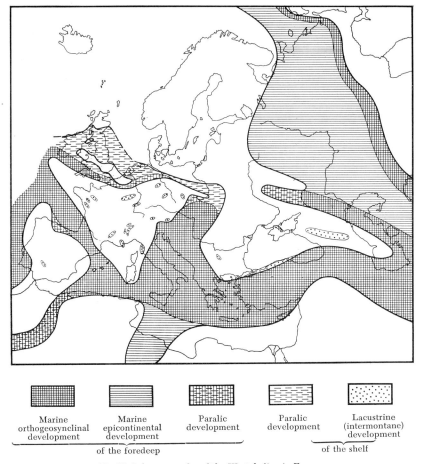

| Marine orthogeosynclinal development | Marine epicontinental development | Paralic development | Paralic development | Lacustrine (intermontane) development |

of the foredeep   of the shelf

Fig. 17. Paleogeography of the Westphalian in Europe

Sudetia and the Svientokrzyz Hills of central Poland. The succession of the Upper Silesian basin is thickest at the foot of eastern Sudetia and becomes thinner and less complete toward the E. The first coal seams occur very deep, in the paralic Ostrau beds. Above the Sattelflöz group, which is distinguished by a single coal seam of up to 30 m., marine intercalations are lacking. The coal reserves in this basin, most of which is still unexplored, have been estimated to a depth of 1000 m. at 65 billion tons.

The inner basins contain a rich development of Stephanian and Lower Permian, but lack marine intercalations; this contrasts with the foredeep, where sedimentation was curtailed by the Asturian phase. The Carboniferous deposits of the *Saar basin* reach the surface only to a small extent. They probably continue in the subsurface from Toul almost as far as the Rhine. The chief coal measures lie in gray Westphalian, though the dominantly red Stephanian, which lies above with slight unconformity, also contains a few workable seams.

In *central Germany,* the Saale trough occupies the same structural situation as the Saar basin, but is a little later in time. Coal seams occur only in the uppermost strata, which are mostly red.

Sudetia. The Inner Sudetian (Lower Silesian) basin contains a nearly complete Carboniferous section. Subsidence began in the Kulm and proceeded into the Rotliegend, with continued widening of the area of deposition. Only the lowest and middle Upper Carboniferous is rich in coal. For the rest barren fanglomerates and arkoses, which originated in arid times, predominate. The Asturian phase reintroduced eruptions. The granitic masses of Sudetia with their lamprophyric dike succession belong to this phase; as also a few porphyry extrusions.

Bohemian and Upper Rhine Massifs. Continental basins formed late and slowly in the Moldanubian zone. Much of the crystalline area remained uplifted even into the Rotliegend. The basal beds of the Plzen-Kladno district west of Prague, marked by a few thick coal seams, belong to the highest Westphalian. The Upper Carboniferous of the Black Forest and Vosges is on the whole still later. In two zones of subsidence variegated arkoses and silts accumulated. There are virtually no workable coal seams.

Numerous small coal basins are scattered over the *Central Massif.* Investigation of these during the last century has told us much about the formation of coal seams and the fossil flora and stratigraphy of the Upper Carboniferous and Permian. The most significant basins are Autun, Blanzy-Creusot, Commentry, the Loire (with St. Etienne) and Gard. Almost all date from the Stephanian; Westphalian D is developed only locally.

In the **British Isles,** the outer edge of the Variscan chain extends from Boulonnais to the southwestern tips of England, Wales, and Eire. S of this line, in the geosyncline, the Lower Carboniferous is developed as Kulm, and the Upper Carboniferous up to the Westphalian, as the Flözleere facies, i.e. with thicker marine beds than in central Europe. N of this line, the foreland, which was consolidated in the Caledonian era, is covered as in north Belgium and Holland, by coal-bearing deposits, but to a much greater extent.

As in the central European sub-Variscan marginal deep, the Carboniferous section of these areas can be divided into three stages. In the Lower Carboniferous, the Old Red continent was inundated by the shallow sea of the Carboniferous limestone. At the transition to the Upper Carboniferous a widespread delta deposit, Millstone grit, was deposited as a consequence of an uplift. It consists of sandstones and shales which spread into a shallow sea. Finally the coal measures were formed in swamps and estuaries as a result of decreasing epeirogenesis. As in the sub-Variscan marginal deep, sedimentation was interrupted at the end of the Westphalian. Stephanian is not known for certain. In both the Lower and the Upper Carboniferous the facies vary from S to N because of decreasing marine influence. In southern England marine and paralic beds predominate; in Scotland, brackish and lacustrine. Thus in the classical Bristol region the Carboniferous limestone consists of dark, fossiliferous crinoidal and oölitic limestones, between which are intercalated brachiopod coquina layers, bryozoan and algal reefs, or fine-grained lagoonal sediments. In Scotland unfossiliferous dolomites, marls, and oil-shales were deposited at the same time. The Upper Carboniferous of southern and central England contains marine intercalations which in many cases are of the same age as those in the Ruhr. Scotland experienced only one great inundation, that of the Aegir horizon; the rest of the sequence is lacustrine. The coal reserves of the British Isles, which are distributed in a great number of basins from Kent to Scotland and Ireland, are estimated at almost 100 billion tons.

Alps and southern Europe. To the S of the Moldanubian zone of the Variscan mountains one again reaches a region with thick Paleozoic deposits which extended beyond the Mediterranean as far as the margin of the African platform. This paleo-Dinaric zone was also folded at the close of the Paleozoic, and indeed, with no less intensity than the rest of the Variscan chain. The folding here, however, did not lead to rigidification. The crust remained mobile, and directly after the mountain-building was again flooded; it now established the pattern for the configuration of the sea in the Mesozoic. Thus in southern Europe, the remains of the Variscan geosyncline were at the transition of the Westphalian to the Stephanian transformed into the geosyncline of the Alpine era. Tethys thereby assumed its ultimate shape.

In the Alps and in southern Europe the Lower Carboniferous is found in more or less the same localities as the Devonian. In the eastern Alpine graywacke zone, calcareous Lower Carboniferous outcrops beside sandy-shaly beds of the same age. On the other hand, in the Carnic Alps, the Balkans, Corsica, in southern France, and on the Iberian peninsula, the Kulm facies predominates. Further S, in North Africa, one reaches an area of epeirogenic stability with development of Carboniferous limestone, which to a certain degree corresponds with that of northwestern Europe.

The paleogeography of the older Upper Carboniferous has not yet been clarified because of the scarcity of marine deposits. In the Grecian archipelago, in the Dinaric and Carnic Alps as well as in upper Hungary the Auernig beds of the latest Upper Carboniferous transgressed with plant-bearing conglomerates and sandstones, which were followed by marine limestones and shales. These filled a marine basin, which represented the beginning of the Alpine geosyncline. Even the fauna commonly shows widespread affinities. A foraminiferal group, the fusulines, were widely distributed and occur as rock-builders.

Northern and eastern Europe. The northern European block, which had been fused together by the Caledonian folding, since the Devonian had divided into the rising Fennoscandia (p. 40), on the one hand, and into the sedimentation realms of the British Isles and Russian platform on the other. Fundamentally this same pattern is true for the Carboniferous. Beds of this age are lacking on the Fennoscandian Shield; they occur, toward the W, in England and Scotland, and toward the E, in Russia.

The Russian platform was shaped as in the Devonian, only it now lay almost fully under sealevel. Shallow-water marine deposits, especially fossiliferous limestones, predominate. Only in the littoral parts, as near Moscow, did the formation of coal take place, as a result of the retreat of the coastline. The margins of the platform were inclined toward the geosyncline in the E and S, and the thickness increased. The filling of the Donetz basin consists of 8000 m. of limestones, sandstones, and shales. Coal seams which extend from the Upper Viséan through the entire Upper Carboniferous, but accumulated as in central Europe in the Westphalian.

Arctic. The Lower Carboniferous, like the Devonian, consists of continental sandstones, only the red and variegated colors are replaced by gray or white. In the Upper Carboniferous, the sea intruded and divided the Old Red continent into a Greenlandian and Fennoscandian block.

General Features

Climate and environment. The Carboniferous contains the greater part of the world's coal reserves. Toward the end of the Paleozoic, coal formation moved outward like a wave from the Arctic through Europe and North America, and diminished across Asia toward the southern continents. The oldest workable seams are known in the Upper Devonian of Bear Island. The deposits of Spitzbergen, Moscow, and the Urals followed in the Lower Carboniferous. With the Upper Carboniferous, coal formation began in the foredeeps and inner basins of Europe and North America. Locally, as in Scotland and Silesia, the lower Namurian is already productive. Considered in general the Middle Westphalian is the richest. A little later, red colors appear in the accompanying rocks. The coal seams diminish; only in a few localities, as in the Saar basin, the Central Massif and Asturia, is Stephanian coal mined.

The causes of the richness of coal in the Carboniferous were equally of biologic- and climatic-, as well as tectonic kinds. In this period plants ultimately colonized the continent. This occurred at a time, which through a mild climate and widespread epeirogenic subsidence, offered especially favorable possibilities for the formation and preservation of plant material.

Crustal movements and magmatism. The formation of the Variscan Mountains took place chiefly during the Carboniferous. The Sudetian orogenesis closed the preceding geosynclinal epoch. The main folding was followed by the formation and filling of the foredeeps, which were joined to the older chains by the Asturian orogeny. The growth of mountains was accompanied by extensive emergence and regression. The end of the Westphalian was a highly geocratic period. Later, in the uppermost Carboniferous, the Stephanian transgression reclaimed certain areas.

Lower Permian

Stephanian   Transgression (southeastern Europe, Arctic)

~~~~~~~~~Asturian folding phase (sub-Variscan foredeep, Asturia, Pyrenees)

Westphalian   Regression (sub-Variscan foredeep, British Isles)

Namurian   Transgression (southeastern Europe)

~~~~~~~~~Sudetian folding phase (Variscan Mountains in central and southern Europe)

Regression (Variscan geosyncline, British Isles)

Viséan   Maximum distribution of Carboniferous seas

Transgression (British Isles)

Tournaisan   Transgression (British Isles, Russia)

~~~~~~~~~Bretonian folding phase (southern Rhenish Schiefergebirge)

Upper Devonian

The diabasic geosynclinal volcanism of Devonian time continued into the oldest Lower Carboniferous. Then the composition of the magma changed. The foldings, particularly the Sudetian, were accompanied by an ascent of granitic plutonic rocks; porphyric extrusives followed in the higher Upper Carboniferous and Permian.

Retrospect. The Variscan folding, which was divided into a series of individual phases, left its imprint on the occurrences of the Carboniferous. In the areas surrounding the mountains widespread uplifts occurred. In central and western Europe a continental episode commenced which lasted until the Jurassic. Even the richness of coal, which gave the Carboniferous its name, is due to the combined effects of tectonics and climate.

Karbon

Stufe	Leitfossilien			Subvariscische und Rhenoherzynische Zone							Saxothuringische Zone			Britische Inseln		Russland	Ostalpen	Nordamerika		
	Goniatiten	Fusulinen Korallen	Pflanzen Brachiopoden	Belgien	Aachen	Ruhrgebiet, Sauerland	Ostrand d. Rhein.Schiefergeb.	Oberharz	Unterharz-Halle	Oberschlesien, Ostsudeten	Saargebiet	Thüringen-Sachsen	Westsudeten	Mittelengland	Schottland	Moskauer B.	Karn. A.	Appalachen	Midcontinent	Texas

endes: Marathonites — Pseudoschwagerina — Callipteris — Unterkreide (Belgien) — Oberkreide (Aachen) — Zechstein — 450m Obere Wettiner / 200m Untere Sch. / 700m Mansfelder Schichten — Rotliegend — Rotliegendes — Rotliegendes — Unterperm (Schwagerinenst) — Unterperm (Rattend.Sch) — Unterperm (Dunkard öd Upper Barren Coal meas.) — (Big Blue) — (Wolfcamp)

Stephan (C, B, A): Uddenites, Prouddenites, Eothalogssoceras / Schistoceras / Triticites / Callipteridium pteridium, Odontopteris, Pecopteris arborescens — Osnabrück — 200m Sch.v.Ohrenkammer, 1700m Ottweiler Schichten, Holzer Kongl. / 100m Radowenzer Sch., 800m Hexensteinarkose, 100m Idastollner Sch. — Oberkarbon C3, Uralstufe, Gshel (Omphalotrochus-Sch.), Kasimov (Tegulifera-Sch.) — Monongahela (Upper Productive Coal measures), Conemaugh (Lower Barren Coal measures) — Virgil, Missouri — Cisco, Canyon

Westfal (D, C, B, A): Wellerites, Owenoceras, Gastrioceras, Paralegoceras, Branneroceras / Fusulina, Fusulinella / Neuropteris ovata, Neuropteris attenuata, scheuchzeri, Lonchopteris rugosa, Sphenopteris hoeninghausi — Assise de Flénu (Fl.Petit Buisson), Assise de Charleroi (Fl.Quaregnon Inf.), Assise d'Andenne — 500m Velener Sch., Ibbenbührener Sch., 200m Dorstener Sch., Merksteiner Sch., Alsdörfer Sch., Kohlschneider Sch. / 700m Piesbergsch., 1500m, 1000m, 400m Horster Sch. (Fl.Ägir, Gasflammk) Fl.L, 500m Essener Sch. (Gask) Fl.Katharina, 600m Bochumer Sch. (Fettk) Fl.Plasshofsbank, 400m Wittener Sch. (Esk) Fl.Sarnsbank, 600m Sprockhöveler Sch. (Magerk) — Rotliegend: 200m Libiazer Sch., 3000m Müldengruppe, 600m Chelmer Sch., 1200m Nikolaier Sch., 400m Rudaer Sch., 150m Sattelgruppe — 2200m Saarbrücker Schichten — 250m Sch.v.Zwickau-Lugau, Sch.v.Flöha, 250m Weissteiner Sch. — 200m Schwadowitzer Schichten, 600m Schatzlarer Sch. (Hangendzug) — 800m Upper Coal, 1000m Middle measures, 300m Lower — Morganian, Ammanian, Lanarkian: 700m Barren Red, Coal measures, Fl.Mansfield, Fl.Amman, Fl.Skipsey band, 1000m Productive Coal measures, 200m Upper Millstone grit — Mittelkarbon C2: 180m Moskaustufe Podolsk, Kaschira, Vereja, Baschkirische (Kajalische) Stufe — Pennsylvanian: Allegheny (Lower Productive Coal measures), Kanawha, New River, Pottsville, Pocahontas — Des Moines, Atoka, Morrow — Strawn, Lampasas, Sloan

Namur (C, B, A): Reticuloceras, Homoceras, Eumorphoceras / Millerella / Neuropteris schlehani u. Mariopteris acuta, Florensprung, Sphenopteris adiantoides — Assise de Chatelet, 250m Assise d'Andenne, 100m Assise de Chokier — Stolberger Schichten, Walhorner Sch. — 1000m Ziegelschiefer, 1000m Flözleeres, 75m Hangende Alaunschiefer, 30m Tonschiefer — -1000m Kulmgrauwacke — 400m Hagener Sch., 600m Arnsberger Sch. — 600m Yeadonian, Marsdenian, Kinderscoutian, Millstone grit, Sabdenian — Upper grit — 100m L.Millst.gr., Upper Limestone gr., Limestone coal gr. — 40m Prolwa — Poca-hontas — Springer — Bend

Dinant (III, II, I): Goniatites (Glyphioceras) γ β α, Pericyclus γ β α, Gattendorfia / D3 Dibunophyllum, D2, D1, S2 Seminula, S1, C2, C1, Z2 Zaphrentis, Z1, K Kleistopora / Productus giganteus, Productus pinguis, Pr.productus, Prod.cora, Productus corrugatus, Pr.sublaevis, Spirifer konincki, Spirifer tornacensis, Spir.strunianus — 500m Schichten v.Bioul u.Warnant, 300-400m Stufe v.Visé, Sch.v.Namêche, 100m Sch.v.Celles, Stufe v.Tournai, Sch.v.Maredsous — 70m Oberer Kohlenkalk, 30m Vaughanitesoolith, 70m Dolomithorizont — 75m Plattenkalk, 20m Posidonienschiefer, 50m Kieselkalk, 15m Lydite, 25m Liegende Alaunschiefer, 3m Hangenbergkalk — 300-900m Kulmgrauwacke, 80m Posidonienschiefer u.Alaunschf., 15m Kieselschiefer, Kalk v.Erdbach, 30m Deckdiabas, 10m Liegende Alaunschiefer — -400m Wechsellagerung, 40m Tonschiefer u.Alaunschf., 50m Adinolst., Kiesel-schiefer Lyditst., 20m Alaunschiefer — Kulmgrauwacke, 100m Kulmkieselschiefer, 150m Bruchberg-Ackerquarzit — 700m Grätzer Grauwacke, 400m Hultschiner Sch., 800m Wagstädter Sch., 1500m Mohrataler Schiefer, 500m Bennischer Grauwacke — 1200m Kulmgrauwacke, 700m Wechsellagerung (Grauwacken u.Schiefer), 150m Unt.Kohlenkalk, 10m Dachschiefer u.Kohlenkalk, 10m Russschiefer (Geigenschiefer), 5m Tonflaserkalk — 250m Kulmgrauwacke, 250m Kulmtonschiefer, Ob.Kohlenkalk, 100m Unt.Kulm, Gneiskongl., 1m Gattendorfiakalk — 1000m Carboniferous Limestone, Upper Carboniferous sandstone, Carboniferous limestone (Avonian), Lower Limest sh. — Arnsbergian, Pendleian, Upper limestone gr., Lower Limestone gr., Oil shale group, Calciferous sandstone, Cement-stone group — Unterkarbon C1: 40m Venev, Oka-stufe Michailov Aleksin, Tula, Tschernyschinostufe, Upa, Malevka-Murajewna — Sch.v.Nötsch (ca 300m) — Mauch Chunk, Greenbrier, Pocono, Waverleyan, Kinderhook — Tarussa, Tennesseeean, Chester, Meramec, Osage, Greenbrier — Bend

des: Wocklumeria / Spir.strunianus — Oberdevon (St.v.Etroeungt) — Oberdevon (Unt.Kohlenk.) — Oberdevon (Hangenbergschiefer) — Oberdevon (Clymenienkalk u.Cypridinenschiefer) — Oberdevon (Engelsberger Sch.) — Oberdevon (Clymenienkalk) — Oberdevon (Ob.Old Red) — Lichwinstufe — Devon-Krist. — Oberdevon (Catskill) — Oberdevon (Chattanooga)

Plate 6. Lower Carboniferous index fossils

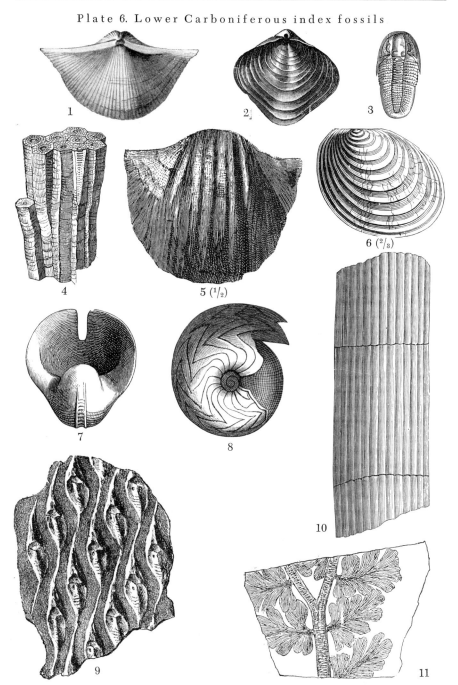

Tournaisan: 1. *Spirifer tornacensis* DE KON. 2. *Athyris lamellosa* LEV. 3. *Phillipsia gemmulifera* PHILL. Viséan: 4. *Lithostrotion basaltiforme* PHILL. 5. *Productus (Gigantoproductus) giganteus* MART. 6. *Posidonia becheri* BRONN. 7. *Bellerophon bicarenus* LEV. 8. *Goniatites crenistria* PHILL. 9. *Lepidodendron veltheimi* STERNB. 10. *Asterocalamites scrobiculatus* SCHLOTH. pith cast. 11. *Sphenopteridium dissectum* GÖPP.

Plate 7. Upper Carboniferous index fossils

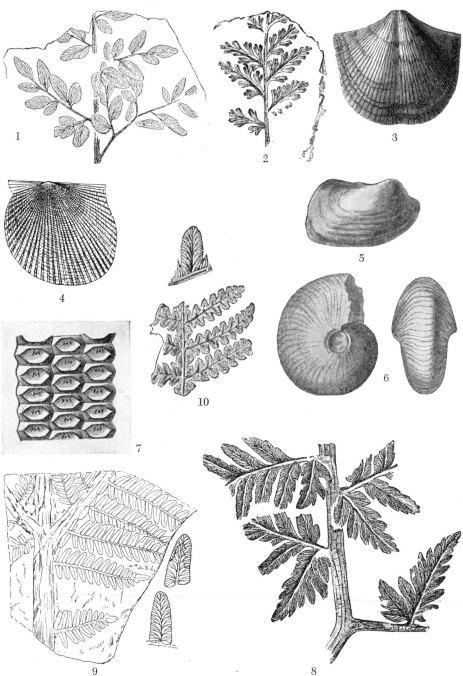

Namurian: 1. *Adiantites oblongifolius* GÖPP. 2. *Sphenopteris adiantoides* SCHLOTH. Westfalian: 3. *Spirifer (Choristites) mosquensis* FISCHER v. WALDH. 4. *Pterinopecten papyraceus* SOW. 5. *Anthracomya modiolaris* SOW. 6. *Homoceras diadema* GOLDF. 7. *Sigillaria elegans* BRONGN. 8. *Mariopteris muricata* SCHLOTH. 9. *Neuropteris (Imparipteris) attenuata* L. & H. Stephanian: 10. *Callipteridium pteridium* SCHLOTH.

The Variscan folding created the marginal troughs and inner basins, on whose slowly subsiding crust swamps could thrive. Coal formation was promoted by a moist subtropical climate of great uniformity, that was favorable for plant growth as well as the preservation of organic deposits.

Supplementary Articles

F. Demanet: Faune et stratigraphie de l'étage Namurien de la Belgique. Mém. Mus. R. Hist. Nat. 97. 1941. Westphalien. Also 101. 1943.

W. Gothan and W. Remy: Steinkohlenpflanzen. Essen 1957.

P. Kukuk: Geologie des niederrheinisch-westfälischen Steinkohlengebiets. Berlin 1938.

H. Paul: Schrifttum des Unterkarbons. Abh. Reichsamt f. Bodenforschg., N. F. H. 198. 1944.

A. Renier: Flore et faune houillères de la Belgique. Musée R. hist. nat. Brüssel 1938.

E. Spengler: Über die Abtragung des varistischen Gebirges in Sachsen. Abh. Geol. Landesanst. Berlin, N. F. 212. 1949.

H. Stille: Das mitteleuropäische variszische Grundgebirge im Bilde des gesamteuropäischen. Beih. Geol. Jb. 2. 1951.

Compte rendu du Congrès pour l'avancement des études de stratigraphie carbonifère. I. Kongress, Heerlen 1927. Maastricht 1928. II. Kongress, Heerlen 1935. Maastricht 1938. III. Kongress, Heerlen 1951. Maastricht 1952. IV. Kongress, Heerlen 1958.

Chapter 8.

Permian

Preliminary Remarks

Boundaries and classification. The oldest attempts at stratigraphic classification are connected with the Permian rocks. In the middle of the 18th century from knowledge of mines in the Mansfeld Kupferschiefer, J. G. Lehmann and G. Chr. Füchsel developed the stratal succession of the Permian of central Germany which was taken over by A. G. Werner in his system. The designations Rotliegend and Zechstein, which had been used by the old German miners, then acquired their geological significance.

R. I. Murchison (1841) discovered that these formations represented an independent period standing between the Carboniferous and Triassic, when he found widespread deposits of the same age in the province of Perm, on the west flank of the Urals. The name Permian, however, could not be displaced by the term Dyas, which had been proposed later by J. Marcou and H. B. Geinitz in consideration of the German conditions.

In central Europe, the cessation of the coal measures and the occurrence of red-colored sediment serves as the basis for dividing the Permian from the Carboniferous. The final withdrawal of the Zechstein sea acts as a useful time indicator at the top. The system lacks these peculiarities in the oceanic development; here the classification is based chiefly on biostratigraphic grounds.

Distribution. The epeirogenic uplifts which resulted from the Variscan folding allowed large land areas to become dry. Continental and marine-epicontinental deposits are therefore widespread in the Permian. The classical region for this development is Germany, where knowledge of the Rotliegend has been advanced particularly by E. Weiss, E. Beyrich, F. Beyschlag, H. Potonié, and H. Falke; that of the Zechstein, by J. K. Freiesleben, H. B. Geinitz, C. Ochsenius, and J. H. van't Hoff. The strata deposited in the open sea were first investigated in Russia (A. P. Karpinsky, Th. Tschernyschew, and B. Licharew). Further important areas are the Carnic Alps (G. Stache, G. Geyer, F. Heritsch, and F. Kahler), and Sicily (G. G. Gemellaro and M. Gortani).

Principal Regions (Fig. 18—20)

Rotliegend in central Europe. The Sudetian orogeny, as remarked on p. 49, introduced an epoch of large-scale undulations of the central European crust. Beginning with the Upper Carboniferous, ridges and basins originated, whose outlines became adapted to the structure of the folded substratum. They commenced at first as single, circular areas of subsidence. During the highest Upper Carboniferous and the Rotliegend, however, they became elongated, united with one another, widened, and deepened. In general a picture emerges of an epeirogenic warping, determined by the structure and mobility of the basement, which during the course of the Rotliegend, gradually flattened and died out with increasing consolidation of the crust. The orogenic phases, the Asturian in the higher Upper Carboniferous and the Saalian between the Lower and Upper Rotliegend, formed short-lived interruptions in this process. They caused fault-folding and blockfaulting without any considerable influence on the course of epeirogenesis.

The volcanic processes were intimately related to tectonic movements. Chiefly melaphyres and quartz porphyries were raised; moderately silicic rocks are rare. The magmas are distinguished from those of the Carboniferous by a greater K-content and belong, therefore, to a Pacific-Mediterranean transitional province. Considered areally, the larger the basin and the greater the thickness of its filling, the more the proportion of eruptives increases. Only the north German basin remained apparently free of volcanic activity. Considered temporally the maximum of the upwellings occurred in each case shortly before the folding phases. The peak of volcanic activity took place in the later Lower Rotliegend, which commonly for that reason is classified as Middle Rotliegend. In addition to effusive layers, subvolcanic laccoliths and sills, locally formed small plutons. In the Erzgebirge, in the Saalian phase, silicic granites rich in

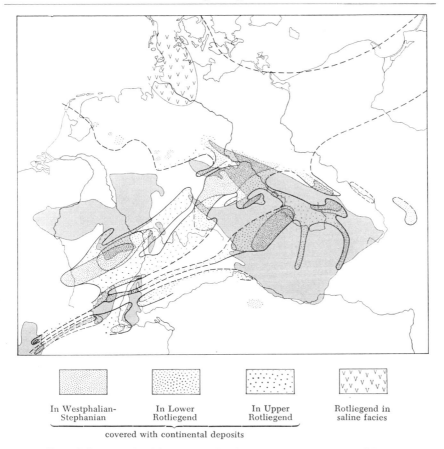

In Westphalian-Stephanian	In Lower Rotliegend	In Upper Rotliegend	Rotliegend in saline facies

covered with continental deposits

Fig. 18. Paleogeography of the Upper Carboniferous and Rotliegend in central Europe

volatile substances were emplaced as the youngest Variscan plutonic rocks; these were significant as ore-bringers ("Tin-granite").

The trough areas of the Upper Carboniferous-Rotliegend were continental, intermontane geosynclines; only the north German basin was for a time reached by the sea. The constitution of the deposits varies considerably with the composition of the erosional areas, the gradient, the kind of transportation, and the distance from the basin margin. In the absence of fossils therefore, stratigraphic classification follows a climatic basis. As did the Stephanian, the basal Lower Rotliegend oscillated between moist and semi-arid. Dark shales with fish and plant remains, coaly sandstones, bituminous limestones and thin coal-seams were deposited in sluggish water courses, in lakes, and ponds; these were covered by brownish-red siltstones and sandstones when desiccation occurred. Aridity increased in the younger Lower Rotliegend and reached its highest degree in the Upper

Rotliegend. Bright red replaced the brownish and grayish colors. Inter-mittent rivers deposited coarse-grained, little-sorted masses of débris con-taining unweathered felspars; also isolated traces of wind action have been recognized. The Upper Rotliegend in many localities consists of typical fanglomerate, which commonly were derived from eruptives and tuffs, that had been deposited shortly before.

North Germany. The North German depression occupies a special place among the Rotliegend basins because of its size, E—W strike, position on a substratum that was folded before the Variscan era, sediment thickness, and occasional flooding. It was the forerunner of the Zechstein sea and the Baltic Strait (p. 85). In the lower Elbe valley more than 1000 m. of red clay with salt layers was deposited, obviously under temporary incur-sions of seawater from the North Sea area.

West and central Germany. The Central German axis (p. 45) lost its position as an uplift area as a result of the Sudetian orogeny. It was over-folded by the sedimentary zones in the NW and SE, deeply depressed, and covered by the Upper Carboniferous-Lower Permian deposits of the Saar- and Saale basins. In the Saar basin, the Kusel- and Lebach beds belong to the moist periods of the Rotliegend; the rich fish- and amphibian fauna of the Lebach clay ironstone nodules is well known. In the country around Halle, the Saale basin was filled predominantly with porphyric extrusives. The white sands of the Weissliegend belong to the youngest Lower Per-mian; these accumulated locally as dunes before the flooding of the Zech-stein sea.

In the *Central Massif*, in contrast to the Stephanian, the Rotliegend is confined more to the marginal parts. The Upper Rotliegend rests uncon-formably on, and markedly overlaps the rocks of the lower stages, which are recognized by bituminous shales and faint coal seams. In spite of the great thickness, effusive rocks are strikingly rare.

South Germany and Bohemia. Two of the most important troughs of the Central Massif, those of Creusot and Autun, come to the surface again in the Upper Rhine and surround the central gneiss core of the Vosges and Black Forest, which have been uplift areas since the Devonian. Its continuation lies in central Bohemia, where subsidence near Plzen had already begun in Westphalian C.

Zechstein in central Europe. In the Permian, a far-reaching transforma-tion in the structure of the basement took place in central Europe. In addition to the strike of the Variscan folds, new lines arose, especially in E-W and NNE-SSW directions. This revolution had already begun in the Rotliegend. It accelerated at the beginning of the Zechstein. The Germanic basin, which originated in this way, retained its essential configuration into the Tertiary. It was formed by the union of two zones of subsidence, an east-west Baltic and a north-south Rhenish. The area of their crossing, north-western Germany, is characterized by especially large thicknesses of strata.

   These changes also opened renewed routes of access to the sea. As in the Rotliegend, the transgression came from the N via the North Sea. This is indicated by the close affinity between the Zechstein fauna of East

Zechstein des Germanischen Beckens

Unter-abteilungen	Randfazies			Beckenfazies		Eindampfungszyklen
	Nordengland	Ostrand d. Rhein.Schiefergeb.	Thüringen	Werragebiet	Nordhannover	
Hangendes:	Unt. Trias (Unterer Buntsandstein)					
Oberer	100m Upper marls	15m Jüngere Konglomerate; 30m Perm Sandstein u. Grenzsande; 3m Stätebergflöz | 15m Plattendol.	10m Obere Bunte Letten m. Gips; 10m Plattendolomit; 20m Untere Bunte Letten m. Gips	20m Obere Bunte Letten m. Gips; 20m Plattendolomit; 30m Untere Bunte Letten m. Gips; 5m Älteres Steinsalz; 10m Anhydrit	5m Obere Letten; 120m Jüngstes Steinsalz; 1m Pegmatitanhydrit; 15m Roter Salzton; 150m Jüngeres Steinsalz m. Kali-flözen {Riedel (5m) {Ronnenberg (5m); 30m Hauptanhydrit; 5m Grauer Salzton; 10m Kaliflöz Stassfurt; 20m Übergangsschichten; 500m Älteres Steinsalz; 2m Basalanhydrit	4. Zykl. / 3. Zykl. (Leineserie Niedersachsenser); 2. Zykl. (Stassfurt-Serie)
Mittlerer	15m Upper limestone; 25m Middle marls	10m Ältere Konglomerate; Untere Letten; 30m Schaumkalk	15m Hauptdolomit / 40m Riffkalk	10m Braunrot.Salzton; 250m Ältestes Steinsalz m. Kali-flözen {Thüringen (3m); 5m Anhydritknotenschf	10m Stinkschiefer; 20m Ob. Anhydrit; 5m Ältestes Steinsalz; 30m Unt. Anhydrit	1. Zykl. (Werraserie)
Unterer	80m Lower Riff-limest.|kalk; 5m Marl slate; 20m Yellow sands	10m Stinkkalk; 8m Kupferletten; 1m Zechsteinkongl.	5m Zechsteinkalk; ½m Kupferschiefer; ½m Mutterflöz; 1m Zechsteinkongl.	7m Zechsteinkalk; ¼m Kupferschiefer; 1m Zechsteinkongl.	5m Zechsteinkalk; ¼m Kupferschiefer; 1m Zechsteinkonglomerat	
Liegendes:	Oberrotliegend	Älteres Paläozoikum u. Kristallin				

Greenland and Germany. As an interior sea the Zechstein basin was largely dependent on connections with the open sea. Repeated expansions and contractions of the connecting strait divided the Zechstein into four naturally-defined cycles.

The *first cycle* began with the Zechstein transgression. The Zechstein conglomerate rests with sharp unconformity on the folded and truncated Variscan base (Fig. 19). A temporary slight constriction of the North Sea strait changed the Zechstein basin into a euxinitic sea, in which was deposited the Kupferschiefer, a dark, carbonaceous-bituminous shale. The copper derived from the erosion of older ore-deposits and, owing to the hydrogen sulphide content of the stagnant sea water, was precipitated as a finely divided sulphide. With the Zechstein limestone, the circulation with the open ocean became freer and thereby introduced a fauna which consisted chiefly of brachiopods, clams, and snails. The bedded limestones interfinger with algal-bryozoan reefs, which colonized the submarine ridges and the cliffs of the coastal zone. At the beginning of the Middle Zechstein, the channel with the open ocean was narrowed once again, but now under a climate that was becoming arid. By means of a constant inward current from the ocean, the salt content of the evaporating seawater of the north

German basin increased; here a large part of the anhydrite was precipitated. The seawater ultimately evaporated as the Oldest Salt sequence, or Werra series, which extended as far as the lower Rhine and Werra basins.

The *second cycle* began with a repeated opening of the Zechstein basin. At first bituminous-shaly and dolomitic deposits in a normal marine facies were laid down. Upon this, as the channel narrowed again, a second evaporite sequence was built up. Because of its distribution and thickness, this Older Salt sequence, or Stassfurt series, is the most important member of the Zechstein. The site of salt precipitation was thereby moved from the marginal areas of subsidence of the

Fig. 19. Variscan unconformity between steeply dipping Lower Carboniferous shales (Kulm) and nearly horizontal Upper Permian limestone (Zechstein). Schwaara, near Gera (Photo by P. Kukuk)

first cycle into the main North German basin. In the Stassfurt beds a reserve of approximately 3 billion tons of sylvitic-kieseritic and carnallitic potassium salts was originally deposited; an amount corresponding to the potassium content of 1/3000 of that of the world's oceans.

The gray saliferous clay, which introduces the *third cycle*, the Leine series, contains fossils which indicate a return to normal marine conditions. In both the last two cycles, which can well be considered together as the Lower Saxon series, the deepest part of the basin lay between Hannover and Hamburg, as it had previously. But the thickness and degree of evaporation remained smaller. Salts, colored red by disseminated clay sediment, alternate with very pure layers, which perhaps originated by derivation from dissolution of older precipitates that were exposed at the basin

Perm

Abteilungen u. Stufen		Leitfossilien		Voruralische Strasse			Mitteleuropa			Tethys-Geos.
		Ammoniten	Fusulinen	Donez-Senke	Moskauer Becken	Ural-Randsenke	Abt. u. St.	Saargebiet	Thüringer Wald	Karnische Alpen
Hangendes		Otoceras		*Unt. Trias* (Dronowskaja)	*Unt. Trias* (Vetluga)		*Unt. Trias* (Buntsandstein)			Unt. Trias (Seiser Sch.)
Oberes Perm	Chideru (Ochoa)	Cyclolobus	Polydiexodina	150 m Korenewskaja-Sch.	200 m Tatarische Stufe		Zechstein (Thuringien)	300 m Kreuznacher Sch.	Mariner Zechstein	100 m Bellerophon-Sch.
	Basleo (Capitan)	Timorites			100 m Kasan-Stufe / 100 m Ufa-Stufe	200 m Belebei / 500 m Jugov — Kupfersandst.				
Unteres Perm	Sosio (Word)	Waagenoceras	Neoschwagerina	50 m Peresasch-Sch.	100 m Brecciöse Kalke	Solikamsk / Jren / Sars / 500 m Kungur	Ob. (Saxonien)	300 m Söterner Sch. — Grenzmelaphyr	200 m Tambacher Sch.	100 m Grödener Sandstein — Tanviser Breccie
	Artinsk (Leonard)	Perrinites	Parafusulina		80 m Gips-Anhydrit-Dolomit-Sch.	Sylva / Sarana / Sarga / Burzewka / 1000 m Artinsk	Rotliegend	200 m Tholeyer Sch.	300 m Oberhöfer Sch.	300 m Trogkofel-Kalk
	Sakmara (Wolfcamp)	Properrinites	Pseudoschwagerina	50 m Tschernigow-Sch.	50 m Dolomit-Sch. / 30 m Schwagerinen-Kalk	Sterlitamak / Tastuba / 500 m Sakmara / Assel	Unt. (Autunien)	300 m Lebacher Sch. / 600 m Kuseler Sch.	250 m Goldlauterer Sch. / 150 m Manebacher Sch. / 350 m Gehrener Sch.	300 m Rattendorfer Sch. / 1000 m Bozener Quarzporphyr
Liegendes		Uddenites	Triticites	Oberkarbon (Araukariten-Sch.)	Oberkarbon (Gshel-Sch.)	Oberkarbon (Pseudofusulinen-Sch.)	(Stephan)	Oberkarbon (Ottweiler Sch.)	(Sch. v. Öhrenkammer)	Oberkarbon (Auernig sch.)

margins. The Leine series culminated in the predominantly sylvitic potash deposits of Ronnenberg and Riedel. In the *fourth cycle*, the Aller series, potassium salt-formation is only sparse. The salts mix upward more and more with clay and finally pass into the Upper Zechstein siltstone, which

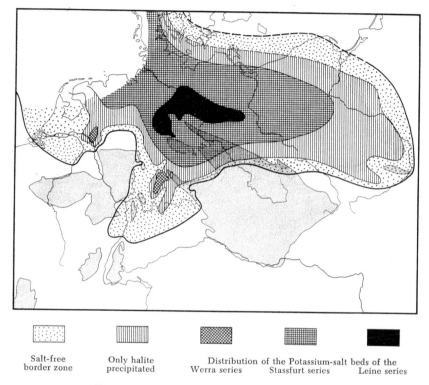

Salt-free border zone	Only halite precipitated	Distribution of the Potassium-salt beds of the
		Werra series	Stassfurt series	Leine series

Fig. 20. Paleogeography of the Zechstein in central Europe

covers the entire salt deposits with an impermeable mantle and forms a transition with the Triassic.

The contours of the *central German uplands* partly coincide with the course of the coast of the Zechstein sea. The Zechstein on the eastern margin of the Rhenish Schiefergebirge, therefore, resembles that in Thuringia and in Saxony, i.e. it possesses a salt-free, partially clastic marginal facies. Algal-bryozoan reefs constitute a Thuringian peculiarity.

In *northwestern Germany* the salt deposits swell to a thickness of nearly 1000 m. During the course of the Mesozoic and Cenozoic, because of the load of the overlying beds and orogenic pressure, the salt migrated into zones of uplift and weakness, anticlines or fractures, and rose in the form of diapirs (Fig. 27, 28).

Northwestern and northern Europe. In the *British Isles,* the Rotliegend (Lower New Red) consists predominantly of red fanglomerates (the brockram), sandstones, and siltstone. Volcanic activity was small. A few basalts and alkalic basalts in Scotland are considered as remnants of the Carboniferous outpourings. Quartz porphyry, which corresponds to that in Germany, occurs only in Cornwall, which was folded in the Variscan era. The Magnesian Limestone filled the inner parts of the British Rotliegend basin and is comparable in its composition to the marginal facies in Germany. In the north of England, as in Thuringia, bryozoan reefs indicate the old coast. Evaporation produced rauchwacke and anhydrite-marls; only in Durham were two salt beds 30 m. thick, formed. These deposits intertongue marginally with variegated marls and sandstones so that beyond the Zechstein basin sharp boundaries are lacking between the Rotliegend, Zechstein, and Triassic.

The discovery of a Rotliegend fauna and flora near *Oslo* moved the extrusive and plutonic rocks of this well-known Atlantic province into the Lower Permian and therefore into the same time-span as the Rotliegend eruptions of central Europe. Probably the rise of the magma was connected with the formation of the Oslo graben.

In **eastern Europe** the rhythms of the Ural folding determined the composition and distribution of the Permian deposits. In the Upper Carboniferous a foredeep originated at the western foot of the mountains, which gradually shallowed toward the W into the epicontinental sea of the Russian platform. In the Lower Permian this basin received up to 5000 m. of sediments. In the Sakmarian these consisted chiefly of limestones and reef limestones. In the Artinskian sandstones and conglomerates won the upper hand and signaled the approach of the Saalian phase, which concluded in the folding of the Urals and its marginal deep. A widespread emergence, which reached its climax in the Triassic, followed the orogeny. In the Kungurian the channel in front of the Urals narrowed and closed. Only an impoverished fauna of an inland sea remained from the rich animal world that had colonized the open sea of the Lower Permian — a fauna which was distinguished by the preponderance of fusulines, brachiopods, and ammonoids. Evaporation occurred, which in a few zones of subsidence, on the northern margin of the Donetz basin (Bachmut) and in front of the Urals (Solikamsk), left significant salt beds deposited. The Zechstein transgression once again created a shallow sea, whose deposits towards the mountains in the E passed into coal beds and the continental red Copper sandstone. After the withdrawal of the last inundation a broad depression remained which was filled with variegated deposits and which retained a few brackish water lakes. Quadrupeds and plants with congenital affinities with those of Texas and the southern continents colonized the region.

In the **Arctic** a withdrawal of the sea followed the Stephanian transgression; the distribution of marine Lower Permian is limited. In the Upper Permian, however, a great flood proceeded outward from the Arctic basin. This marine invasion extended into Russia as the sea of the Kazanian stage and into Germany as the Zechstein sea; it even reached Nova Scotia.

Alps and southern Europe. In the western Mediterranean region the continental episode which had been introduced by the Variscan mountain-building endured until the Triassic. Here, as in central Europe, a series of continental basins was formed. In the eastern Mediterranean region, on the other hand, the Alpine geosyncline (p. 54), which originated in the Upper Carboniferous, expanded in the Permian. At the same time marine life became more abundant. Fusulines, corals, brachiopods, and calcareous algae composed entire rock layers and made the Mediterranean Permian by reason of its relationships to the east Asian and Texan faunas a part of the meridional belt of the Tethys sea.

In the Apennines, and in the western and southern Alps, the trough that had been partly created at the end of the Carboniferous enlarged and collected the red, often coarse débris of the Verrucano. Extrusive rocks are rare except for the thick cover of the Bozen quartz porphyry in southern Tyrol. Similar relationships prevail in southern France, Spain, and North Africa.

In the *Carnic Alps* the Lower Permian marine region still nearly coincided with that of the Stephanian; here clastic intercalations receded in the Rattendorf beds and are lacking altogether in the Trogkofel reef-limestone. Gentle crustal movements introduced a new sedimentation cycle which led to the transgressively deposited red Gröden sandstone, and above this followed rauchwacke and the dolomitic Bellerophon limestone. In the latter species of the German Zechstein can be found together with those of the Indian Productus limestone.

From the southern Alps the Permian sea extended over the inner Dinaric chains, Greece, the Aegean, Tunis and Sicily to the Balearic Islands and made short-lived transgressions toward Tuscany, Elba, and the Glarus Alps.

General Features

Climate and environment. The Permian deposits of the northern hemisphere show numerous indications of a warm, even hot, and increasingly arid climate. The Rotliegend facies with its arkoses and fanglomerates must have originated under semi-arid conditions. Owing to its thick rock-salt and potash-salt deposits the Permian was the most important time

Plate 8. Permian index fossils

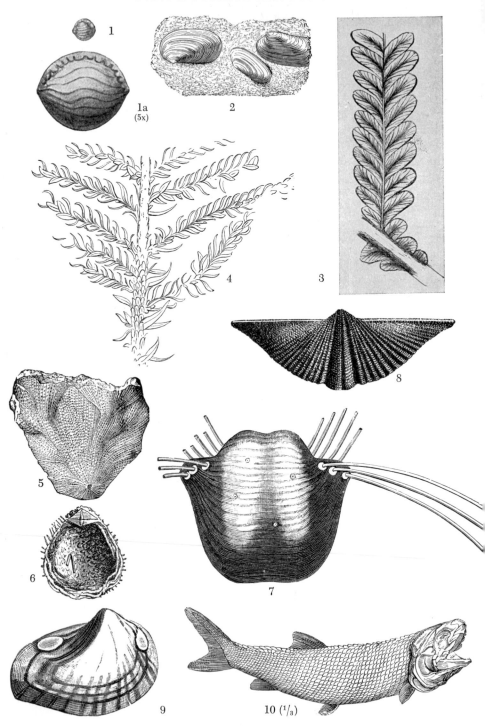

1

1a
(5x)

2

3

4

5

6

7

8

9

10 ($^1/_3$)

Lower Permian: 1, 1a. *Pseudoschwagerina* sp. (= *Schwagerina* aut.). 2. *Anthracosia carbonaria* GOLDF. 3. *Callipteris conferta* BRONGN. 4. *Lebachia* (= *Walchia* aut.) *piniformis* STERNB. Upper Permian: 5. *Fenestella retiformis* SCHLOTH. 6. *Strophalosia goldfussi* MÜNST. 7. *Productus horridus* SOW. 8. *Spirifer alatus* SCHLOTH. 9. *Schizodus obscurus* SOW. 10. *Palaeoniscus freieslebeni* AG.

for salt-formation in the geologic past. The great geosynclines, especially Tethys, were colonized by a rich warm-water fauna. How these phenomena are harmonized with the widespread evidence of a Permo-Carboniferous ice age in the southern hemisphere is meanwhile unexplained.

Crustal movements and magmatism. The Permian includes the dying out of the Variscan era of folding, which closed with the Saalian phase as the last intense orogenesis. The mountain-building was accompanied by an increasing regression, which began in the Upper Carboniferous and reached its climax in Upper Permian-Lower Triassic time. At the beginning of the Mesozoic the sea was almost completely crowded back into the great geosynclines. This shrinkage of the surface of the sea demonstrated especially clearly the change which the Earth had passed through since the Middle Carboniferous. Tethys, the mother-geosyncline of the Alpine mountains, had originated from the Variscan areas of subsidence.

Lower Triassic

                    Regression (Germanic and Russian Zechstein basins)

Zechstein   Transgression (Germanic and Russian Zechstein basins, Carnic Alps, southeast Europe, northern Caucasus)

Upper Rotliegend

            ~~~~~~~~~Saalian folding phase (Urals)

Lower Rotliegend   Regression (Carnic Alps, southeast Europe, Ural foredeep)

Upper Carboniferous

As the folding declined volcanic outbursts also slackened. The majority of the prevailingly porphyric eruptions fell in the Lower Rotliegend. With the Zechstein a long time without volcanic activity embracing the whole Mesozoic, began for central Europe.

Retrospect. Measured in years the Permian was considerably shorter than the preceding periods. Its individuality is therefore less marked, especially as it presents from a tectonic viewpoint the direct continuation of the Carboniferous. Magmatic activity expired with the last phases of the Variscan folding.

Supplementary articles

E. Fulda: Zechstein. Handb. vgl. Stratigr. Deutschlands, Berlin 1935.

F. Lotze: Steinsalz und Kalisalze. Berlin 1957.

J. F. Pompeckj: Das Meer des Kupferschiefers. Branca-Festschrift. Leipzig 1914. 444.

G. Richter: Geologische Gesetzmäßigkeiten in der Metallführung des Kupferschiefers. Arch. Lagerstättenforsch. 73. 1941.

R. L. Sherlock: The Permo-Triassic Formations. London 1947.

Chapter 9.

Triassic

Preliminary Remarks

Boundaries and classification. We owe our first knowledge of the Trias-sic to J. G. Lehmann and G. Chr. Füchsel, who in about 1780 separated the Buntsandstein and Muschelkalk in the Flözgebirge of central Germany, and to E. F. v. Schlotheim, who described its fossil content in 1823. The researches of J. F. L. Hausmann, C. v. Oeynhausen, H. v. Dechen and E. de Beaumont in the first quarter of the last century taught that these sub-divisions, to which L. v. Buch added the Keuper as the uppermost, were widespread also in southern Germany. Here F. v. Alberti in 1834 brought together the three stratigraphic members as the Triassic system. The con-cept found rapid acceptance but it was still a long time until the equi-valent of the Triassic was recognized in the "Alpine limestone". Between 1830 and 1850 L. v. Buch, G. zu Münster, F. v. Hauer, and H. Emmerich shed the first light on this question. The different aspect of the Alpine rocks gave rise in later years to a special classification that was equivalent to the one which had originated in Central Europe.

Distribution. The Triassic was a time of geocraty — that is, of a pre-ponderance of dry land. Broad cratonic areas were blanketed by continen-tal deposits with a few intercalations of shallow marine sediments. The sea was even more limited to the great geosynclines than in the Permian; in them thick marine, predominantly carbonate rock sequences were de-posited. German Triassic and the "Alpine limestone" are typical develop-ments of what is distinguished as the Germanic and Alpine (or pelagic) facies of the Triassic.

The rocks of the Triassic occupy considerable areas of the terrane in central and southern Germany. Among the numerous geologists who occupied themselves after the first investigation, F. A. Quenstedt, K. v. See-bach, A. v. Strombeck, E. W. Benecke, E. Schmid, E. Fraas, F. Thürach, H. Eck, E. Philippi and M. Schmidt were prominent. Further European districts of the Germanic facies are England (R. L. Sherlock), the Swiss Jura and western Alps, the Iberian peninsula, and the western Mediterra-nean region (A. Tornquist, A. Wurm, and M. Schmidt), and finally the Russian platform.

Pelagic deposits predominate in the eastern and southern Alps, where E. Suess, F. v. Richthofen, C. W. Gümbel, E. W. Benecke, E. v. Mojsisovics, A. Bittner, C. Diener, and J. Pia carried out their fundamental investiga-tions.

Principal Regions (Fig. 21—25)

Germanic Triassic in central and northwestern Europe. In Germany and on the British Isles the Upper Permian and Triassic stand in close relationships from the point of view of Earth history. The Germanic basin retained the same form that it possessed when it originated in the Zechstein, and maintained this shape almost until the end of the Triassic. Considered in general, the continental episode of Central Europe which had begun at the end of the Carboniferous with the Variscan folding continued during this period. Epeirogenic changes, which introduced the transgressive period of the Jurassic, first took place in the Rhaetic.

The chief outlines of the framework were determined as in the Permian by the Rhenish and Baltic zones of subsidence (p. 63). During the course of the Triassic the depositional area widened almost constantly. The Buntsandstein extended particularly in the Rhenish trough toward the S, but also covered considerable parts of the adjoining higher areas, notably the Gallic uplift on the W, and to a lesser extent, the Vindelician ridge to the SE. The extension toward the S was connected with a tilting of the entire basin. Toward the end of the Buntsandstein episode of deposition an uplift in the N closed the North Sea strait, which had allowed admission to the Permian seas and the transient ingressions during the Buntsandstein. Instead of these, channels to the Alpine geosyncline opened in the S — the Upper Silesian passage in the Lower Muschelkalk, and the Burgundian in the Upper Muschelkalk. Thus the Germanic basin, once an extension of the Arctic Ocean, came under the influence of Tethys. In the Middle Keuper the depositional area expanded in almost all directions. A new epoch began with the Rhaetic. A far-reaching inundation pushed forward toward central Europe from the British Isles. Orogenic and volcanic occurrences are lacking in the German Triassic.

The deposits of the Buntsandstein can be classified into a series of cycles, as was the Zechstein. Each of them begins, doubtless as a result of a sudden tectonic upheaval, with coarse-grained, and ends with fine-grained, deposits. The spatial arrangement of the facies corresponds to the temporal arrangement. Fluvial conglomerates and sandstones are characteristic of the marginal areas, and marine, brackish or hypersaline siltstones with carbonate, anhydrite, and halite intercalations, of the inner parts of the basins. The Lower Buntsandstein forms a termination of the evaporation epoch of the Zechstein. Shallow, at times saline stretches of water were widespread (Fig. 22). In the Middle Buntsandstein the climate became moister, plant and animal life somewhat richer. Northern Germany was covered by a shallow lagoonal sea, as in the Lower Buntsandstein. The Upper Buntsandstein, or Röt, was already a transitional member

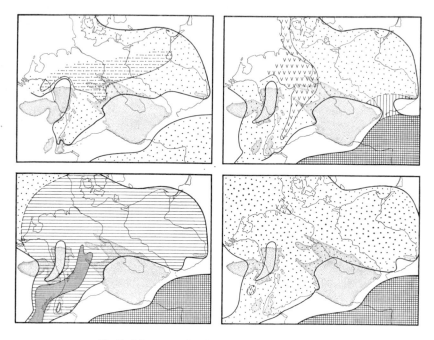

Fig. 21. Paleogeography of the Triassic in central Europe

Upper left: Lower Buntsandstein. Distribution of the Rogenstein: indicated by dot-dash line
Upper right: Upper Buntsandstein. Distribution of the Röt salt: small "V" 's
Lower left: Upper Muschelkalk. Distribution of the sea at the end of the Ceratite-beds: closely
                spaced lines
Lower right: Middle Keuper. Distribution of the Keuper salt: small "V"'s

Fig. 22. Dried and rolled-up clay fragments. Lower Buntsandstein, Marburg

of the Muschelkalk. At first there was a temporary constriction, because of which salt deposits up to 100 m. thick were crystallized out in the deepest parts of the basin. Then, however, a growing area was covered by shallow seawater, which floved in through the Upper Silesian passage. The Muschelkalk sea was an inland waterway in an arid environment. The intense evaporation and the small amount of clastic material gave rise chiefly to carbonate sediments, whereby limestone was deposited in the central parts of the basin, and dolomite in the more concentrated water of the coastal areas. The thinly stratified marly, oölitic, and coquina-limestones of the Lower Muschelkalk, or Wellenkalk, were deposited in a wadden sea which occasionally dried up. The evaporite cycle of the Middle Muschelkalk, as is the Röt salt, is connected with a displacement of the sea-channels, this time from the Upper Silesian to the Burgundian passage. It led to widespread rock-salt precipitation, particularly in the south German sector of the Rhenish trough. At the beginning of the Upper Muschelkalk entire forests of crinoids colonized the sea floor; their remains mixed with shell débris form the Trochitenkalk. Later the sea deepened, the crinoids disappeared and in the layered limestones and marls of the Ceratite beds ammonoids are abundant. The Muschelkalk transgression reached its peak in this stage. Then, however, deltas began to push forward into the shrinking and shallowing basin. Marine dolomitic limestone beds alternate with dark marls and plant-bearing sandstones, now and then even with impure coals, which gave the Lower Keuper the name Lettenkohle. Bright-colored sediments lead into the Middle Keuper, the second continental episode of the German Triassic. Compared with the Buntsandstein the area of sedimentation had become broader and shallower; variegated clays form the bulk of the deposits. In its deeper parts they included gypsum, locally even rock-salt. The brackish to marine beds of the Upper Keuper or Rhaetic show a distinct boundary from the Middle Keuper. The basal part is still greenish. The bone beds intercalated in it consist of bones of continental and marine animals, which were formed as residual concentrates in moving shallow water. Then, however, dark clays and light sandstones brought the bright colors to a close. The transition into the facies of the Lias was thereby accomplished.

The inhabitants of the Germanic Triassic basin in the continental intervals were amphibians and reptiles, of whom commonly only the tracks are preserved, as well as a flora, which in part was adapted to a life on dry and even salt-permeated ground. The colonization of the Muschelkalk sea proceeded from Tethys, but only a fraction of the pelagic fauna became indigenous to the German inland sea. The Rhaetian sea brought

with it a new fauna from Tethys. This was the forerunner of the Jurassic
fauna; only the cephalopods were lacking.

The *British Isles* during the Triassic, as in the Zechstein, belonged to
the higher-standing marginal regions of the basin. They were therefore
reached by neither the sea of the Muschelkalk nor by the ingressions
of the Buntsandstein and those of the Keuper. Only the occurrence of
gypsum and halite in the Middle Keuper of central England indicates
evaporation from lagoons. Apart from this, the aspect of the beds is similar
to that of Germany.

The Germanic Triassic in southwest Europe and North Africa extends
from southwestern Germany through the western Alps and the Rhône
depression toward the S and occupies considerable areas in the lands
marginal to the western Mediterranean. The Helvetic Triassic of the western Alps, because of its position right on the margin of the basin, is
stunted in contrast to the normal section; however, the Vindelician ridge
began to sink gradually from the Muschelkalk onward. The true opening
of the Germanic inland sea lay approximately between Sardinia and North
Africa. From it the Alpine geosyncline built forward toward the W. In the
Betic Cordillera and in the Moroccan Rif the pelagic Upper Triassic overlies the Buntsandstein and Muschelkalk of Germanic development.

Pelagic Triassic of the eastern and southern Alps. We have explained
(p. 54) how the epeirogenic structure of the Mediterranean region inverted
itself in the younger Carboniferous and how the geosynclines of Mesozoic
age came forth from the Variscan zones of subsidence. The origin of the
Alpine geosyncline was the Stephanian-Permian sea of the southern Alps.
From it and by the inclusion of the northern Alps the Triassic depositional
area developed. This area divided into two basins, the south Alpine
and the north Alpine; these were separated by the central Alpine ridge.
The thickness figures, nearly 3000 m. in the basins and scarcely 1000 m.
on the ridge, illustrate the difference in rates of sedimentation. The
Triassic transgression began in the lower Scythian, extended in the Anisian
over the central Alpine ridge into the north Alpine basin, and in the
Ladinian attained a first climax. At the transition to the Karnian broad
areas became dry, but these were re-flooded by the second transgressive
climax coinciding with the Norian. The Rhaetian brought renewed shallowing, now and then even breaks in sedimentation, which were related to
gentle crustal movements. True unconformities however, are lacking.

Volcanic activity is closely related to the tectonic arrangement of the
Alpine geosyncline. In the Middle Triassic the southern Alps were the
scene of extensive outbursts, which yielded tuffs chiefly of andesitic, but
sometimes basaltic, composition. In the north Alpine trough only a few

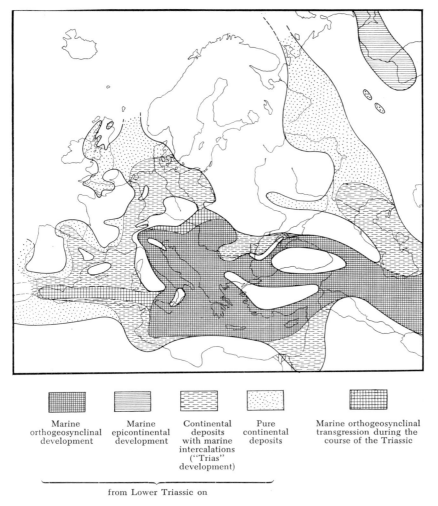

Marine orthogeosynclinal development

Marine epicontinental development

Continental deposits with marine intercalations ("Trias" development)

Pure continental deposits

Marine orthogeosynclinal transgression during the course of the Triassic

from Lower Triassic on

Fig. 23. Paleogeography of the Triassic in Europe

insignificant eruptions have been recognized; in the central Alps they are nearly lacking.

The Triassic sequence of the eastern and southern Alps is marine almost throughout in contrast to the Germanic basin with its predominantly continental deposits. The depth of water and proportion of clastic or chemical components changed simultaneously with movements of the sea. Continental influences appear more intensely in the Scythian and Karnian, whereas the pelagic deposits reach a peak in the Ladinian and Norian stages. The tectonic evolution of the Alpine geosyncline reflects this further, in that the south-Alpine facies preceded the central, and north-

Alpine facies. In the southern Alps the Scythian is already composed of marine deposits; in the N, on the other hand, it consists of bright-colored continental and saline deposits, the Werfen beds, which probably extend back into the Upper Permian. Deposits of the open sea, such as the gray bedded limestones of the Alpine Muschelkalk, the Reifling or Gutenstein limestones first appeared here in the Anisian stage, that is, at a time when the first reefs began to grow in the southern Alps. The differences diminish in the Ladinian. The sea floor over wide areas, even in the northern Alps, was colonized by calcareous algae, and also by reef corals. The pale, carbonate rocks of the Wetterstein limestone, Ramsau dolomite, and Schlern dolomite, which are many hundreds of meters thick, are built up of an alternation of algal biostromes, bioclastic rocks, and finely stratified mud. As a result of the Karnian regression considerable parts of the Alps became dry land and underwent Karst weathering, but not for long. The emerged surfaces sank during the new spread of the sea and were covered with the Raibl beds. At the base lie conglomerates, sandstones, and shales which stemmed from the Vindelician, Bohemian, the central Alpine, and a northern Italian denudation area. Rauchwacke with gypsum follows. At the beginning of the Norian stage thick-bedded limestones and dolomites returned. The Haupt dolomite is a mud rich in foraminifera; its bitumen content is noteworthy; it is locally enriched to asphalt shale deposits. Corals and thick-shelled pelecypods participated in the building of the Dachstein limestone; calcareous algae, which were earlier so widespread are, however, lacking here. The Kössen beds were deposited in the shallow sea of the Rhaetic; these consist of an alternating sequence of dark bedded shelly limestones and marls in uniform development. Only on a few ridges were pale reef limestones affixed, Rhaetian Dachsteinkalk or Upper Rhaetic limestone (Fig. 24).

All faunal groups of the open sea play a part in the Alpine Triassic. The importance of corals and calcareous algae as reef-builders has already been emphasized; in addition, especially the cephalopods and brachiopods should be named. Close affinities exist between the Alpine faunas and those of the remaining great geosynclines, particularly with those of southern Asia.

In the *southern Alps,* particularly in the Dolomites, the Seis and Campill beds, a succession of fine sandy marls and thinly stratified limestones, overlies the Upper Permian Bellerophon-limestone. Upward the marine influence is intensified. As early as the Anisian the first reef-rock, the Mendel dolomite, developed from the bedded Lower Muschelkalk. In the Ladinian the facies contrasts attain their greatest degree because of the introduction of volcanic masses. The Buchenstein beds are developed more or less uniformly as nodular limestones with ash layers (Pietra verde). Then, however, reef-

Pelagische Trias der Ost- und Südalpen

Abteilungen u. Stufen		Germ. Gliederung	Leitfossilien	Bayrisch-Tirolische Alpen (Bayerische F.)	Salzburger Alpen (Berchtesgadener F.) (Hallstätter F.)	Nordöstliche Kalkalpen (Bayer. u. Berchtesgad.)	Zentralalpen (Zentralalpine F.)	Dolomiten	Lombardische Alpen
Hangendes:				Unt.-Mittl. Lias (Fleckenmergel)	Mittl.-Unt. Lias (Hierlatzk) (Fleckenmergel)	Unt.-Mittl. Lias	Lias	Mittl. Lias	Mittl. Lias
Trias	Rätische Stufe	Ob. Keuper	Avicula contorta	150m Kössener Schichten; ~100m Oberrätkalk; ~200m Plattenk.	50m Zlambachmergel; Oberrätkalk; 1000m Dachsteinkalk bzw. Hochgebirgsriffkalk	Oberrätkalk; 100m Kössener Schichten	100m Kössener Sch.	600m Dachsteindolomit	400m Kössener Schichten
	Ober-Norische Stufe	Mittl.		800m Hauptdolomit	800m Dachsteinkalk; 150m Ob. Hallstätter Kalk	500m Hauptdolomit u. Dachsteinkalk	300m Hauptdolomit		600m Hauptdolomit
	Karnische Stufe	Keuper	Protrachyceras aonodes	250m Raibler Schichten	250m Raibler Schichten; 100m Unt. Hallstätter (Draxlehner) Kalk; 20m Cardiltasch	300m Opponitzer Kalk; 300m Lunzer Sandst.; Lunzer Reingrabener Sch.	100m Raibler Sch.	50m Raibler Schichten	400m Raibler Schichten
Mittel-trias	Ladinische Stufe	Unt. Keuper	Pachycardia rugosa; Trachyceras aon	800m Wettersteinkalk; ~200m Partnachsch.	700m Ramsaudolomit	1000m Wettersteinkalk	300m Wettersteindolomit	Pachycar.-200m Olentuffe; 800m Schlern dol.; 250m Marmolata k.; 200m Cassianer Sch.; 200m Wengener Sch.; 40m Buchensteiner Sch.; 80m Mendeldolomit; 25m Unt. Muschelkalk	500m Esinokalk; 800m Esino dol.; 400m Wengener Sch.; Perledo kalk; 200m Buchensteiner Sch.; 100m Mendeldol.; 100m Unt. Muschelk. (Gracilisch)
		Ob. Muschelk.	Daonella lommeli						
		Mittl. Muschelk.	Protrachyceras langobardicum; Protrachyceras reitzi; Dipl. annulatissima						
	Anisische Stufe	Unt. Muschelk.	Cera-Daonella sturi; tites binodosus; Daonella gracilis	300m Muschelkalk; 30m Reichenhaller Sch.	300m Muschelkalk; Reichenhaller Dol.	100m Reiflinger K.; 150m Anis Dol.; 100m Gutensteiner Kalk	100m Reiflinger Kalk; Dolomit u. Rauchwacke; 150m Schreyeralmkalk	Unt. Muschelkalk	
Untertrias	Skythische Stufe	Bunt-sandst.	Tirolites cassianus; Claraia clarai	250m Buntsandsten	300m Haselgebirge; Werfener Sch.	200m Werfener Sch.; 50m Prebichikongl.; 50m Quarzit	50m Quarzit	Campiller Sch.; 250m Seiser Sch.	150m Servino
Liegendes:			Diplopora annulata; Physoporella pauciforata	Kristallin und Paläozoikum		Kristallin und Paläozoikum	Oberperm (Bellerophon)	Oberperm (Bellerophon?) (Gracilisch)	Perm Porphyr

building episodes, during which bioherms that sloped 10°—30°, grew up on submarine ridges, alternated several times with episodes of eruption, during which the depressions were filled with lavas and tuffs (Fig. 25). The Wengen beds contain the greatest proportion of volcanic rocks. In the Cassian beds marly limestone won the upper hand. Extrusive activity ended with the Karnian stage. Large parts of the Dolomites passed through

Fig. 24. Rhaetic coral reefs, passing below and laterally into bedded limestones Steinplatte, northeast Tyrol (after W. Vortisch)

a short-lived interval of subaerial exposure whose red weathering products colored the Raibl beds. Where the sea remained, the Dachstein dolomite extends from the Karnian to the Rhaetic stage. The Lower Triassic flooding first reached the Lombardy Alps with the Campill beds, and the lower part of the Servino consisted of red sandstones. The section of the Middle Triassic is similar to that in the Dolomites; the proportion of volcanic material remained small and is lost entirely toward the W.

In the *central Alps* the moderately thick succession in the Scythian consists of quartzites, and in the higher stages, of dolomites, rauchwackes, and black "pyritic shales". The characteristic of the rocks indicates that parts of the central Alpine ridge during the Triassic emerged repeatedly as islands above sea-level. The sequences at Graubünden, Rhätikon and Engadine is similarly of small thickness. Owing to their position they link the Helvetic, south Alpine and north Alpine facies. The connections, however, were severed by later thrusting movements. Although the lower Pennine Nappes still display Germanic Triassic the region of the root zone of the upper Pennine and the lower east Alpine nappes already belong to Tethys.

The *north-eastern Alps*, in contrast to the southern Alps, which are mostly only gently folded, are composed of a series of thrust sheets lying one above another. If one mentally slides the sheets back into their original positions, then the facies distribution forces the conclusion that the deepest

Fig. 25. Reef facies and volcanic facies in the South Tyrolean Dolomites. Sella and Grödener Joch. Over the Joch is an interbedding of tuffs of the Wengen beds with the Schlern dolomite. Upper snow-covered bench shows the Raibl beds; the Dachstein limestone forms the summits

part of the north Alpine basin must have lain in what is today the southern border of the north-eastern Alps. Remnants of thrust sheets, which originally belonged in this Hallstatt or Juvavian region, are preserved principally in the Salzburg Alps. The first filling of this depression, which began even in the Upper Zechstein, consists of evaporites, the bright-colored anhydritic and halitic clays of the Haselgebirge. In the Lower Triassic the depositional site widened; red clastic rocks, whose grain size diminished toward the top, were distributed over the entire northern Alps. Above the dark, bedded or nodular limestones of the Anisian stage the pale algal reef limestones of the Ladinian Wetterstein limestones were deposited as a result of freer water circulation. On the northern margin of the Alps they interfinger with the gray Partnach marls which were derived from the Vindelician-Bohemian land. At the beginning of the Karnian stage considerable clastic detritus was transported from this higher region as a result of the general uplift of the Alpine geosyncline. The crevices of the Karst surface on the Wetterstein limestone were filled with sandy deposits. On the northern margin of the Alps these incorporate, as the Lunz sandstone, coal seams. Towards the interior of the geosyncline they pass over into marine deposits, Raibl sandstone, Reingraben shales, and finally into the limestone of the Cardita-oölite. In the Norian stage the facies distribution was similar. The Haupt dolomite prevails in the northern, and the Dachstein limestone, in the inner parts of the north-eastern Alps. The Hallstatt region was only little influenced by the Middle and Upper Triassic movements of the sea. The domain of the open sea began here in the Anisian. Algal and coral reef limestones, such as the Ramsau dolomite and the Hochgebirg reef limestone, formed almost without interruption until the Rhaetic. In between the reefs the light-colored Hallstatt limestone, which is known for its cephalopod content, was deposited. Of special note is its small thickness in comparison with the reef rocks; the Ladinian seems to be altogether lacking.

Pelagic Triassic of southern Europe. The eastern and southern Alps belong to the meridional sea, Tethys, which encircled the Earth during the Mesozoic. In the beginning of the Triassic the encirclement was not quite complete, but advanced from the E. The older cephalopod zones of the Scythian are known only from India and Armenia; Tirolites was the first to migrate into the southern Alps. From the Upper Triassic on, the Alpine facies also invaded the western Mediterranean region, where until then the Germanic facies had prevailed (p. 74).

The trough of the northern Alps was connected to the Balkans via the Carpathians. Even the Dobrudsha, which today is part of the foreland, was at that time included in the geosyncline. The south Alpine trough was continued in the great Adriatic geosyncline, which in the Triassic included the Apennines and Dinarides. As in the Permian the entrance for the transgressions and faunas which came from Asia lay here. The Dinaric facies, therefore, preceeds the Alpine. The Lower Triassic is more decidedly marine, Hallstatt limestone occurs even in the Scythian and is widespread in the Anisian. In the Middle Triassic the deepest part of the trough became filled by a thick chert-shale sequence in which green geosynclinal eruptives, serpentine masses, basic flows and tuffs are intercalated.

General Features

Climate and environment. With the Triassic an epoch of more balanced climate began, which continued until the end of the Mesozoic. The most intense warming of the ocean plainly fell in the Middle Triassic. This can be inferred from the distribution of the Diplopores, which are today preeminently indigenous to tropical waters. They were lacking in the Scythian, widespread in the Anisian and Ladinian, but in the Upper Triassic again receded. Most of the continental deposits bear the marks of a semi-arid climate, with occasional tendencies toward greater humidity or aridity. Only at the end of the Triassic was it generally moister and cooler, as proved by the coal-bearing deposits of the Rhaetic and Lias.

Crustal movements and magmatism. Two features are particularly noteworthy in the paleogeography of the Triassic. The first which had been prepared already in the Permian, is the limitation of the seas to the large Alpine geosynclines. Pelagic Triassic is therefore found today almost exclusively in young mountain chains; only in a few localities, as in Dobrudsha, does it overlap the foreland. The other noteworthy feature is the wide distribution of the three-fold "Trias" stratigraphic sequence, e.g. in Germany or Russia. Epicontinental ingressions evidently found easier access to the continental basins than before. The Triassic, mainly a period of geocraty, is subdivided by two transgressions, those of the Scythian and the Karnian-Norian, as well as two regressions, at the end of the Ladinian and at the beginning of the Rhaetic.

Lias	
Rhaetic	Transgression (Germanic basin, western Mediterranean region)
	Regression (Arctic)
Norian	Maximum spread of Triassic sea
	Transgression (western Mediterranean region, Arctic)
Karnian	Transgression (Germanic basin, Alps, Arctic)
	∿∿∿∿∿∿∿Folding phase (Caucasus)
Ladinian	Regression (Germanic basin, Alps, Arctic)
Anisian	Transgression (Germanic basin, Alps)
Scythian	Transgression (Alps, Carpathians, Arctic)
Upper Permian	

Viewed broadly the Triassic was an orogenically quiet period. Magmatic activity was predominantly extrusive; its chemistry moderately silicic to basic. In the marine geosynclines, especially in the Alps and Dinarides, basaltic and andesitic flows and tuffs were brought upward.

Retrospect. The Triassic falls in the span of time between the close of the Variscan and the beginning of the Alpine eras of folding. Mountain-building declined. In some of the large geosynclines the initial volcanism set in with basic extrusives. In general a uniform semi-arid climate prevailed. Only the Rhaetic was a moist and cool age with widespread coal deposits.

6 Brinkmann, Geologic Evolution of Europe

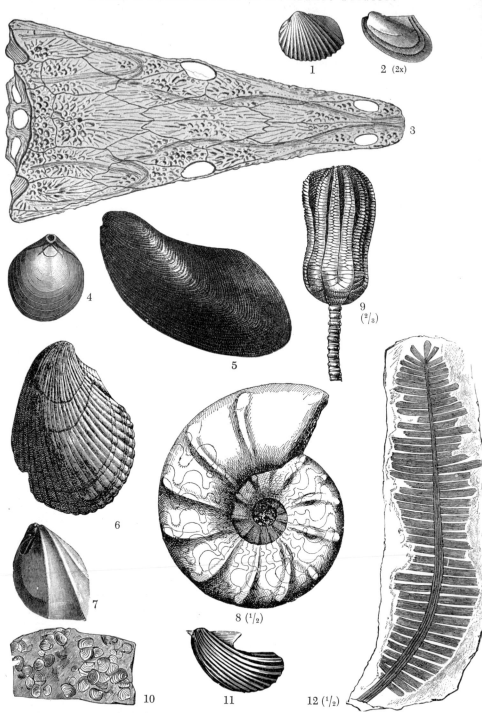

Plate 9. Index fossils of Germanic Triassic

1

2 (2x)

3

4

5

9 (²/₃)

6

7

8 (¹/₂)

10

11

12 (¹/₂)

Buntsandstein: 1. *Myophoria costata* ZENK. 2. *Avicula* (= *Gervilleia* aut.) *murchisoni* GEIN.
3. Skull of *Trematosaurus brauni* BURM. Muschelkalk: 4. *Coenothyris vulgaris* SCHLOTH.
5. *Gervilleia (Hoernesia) socialis* SCHLOTH. 6. *Lima striata* SCHLOTH. 7. *Myophoria vulgaris*
SCHLOTH. 8. *Ceratites nodosus* BRUG. 9. *Encrinus liliiformis* SCHLOTH. Keuper: 10. *Estheria
minuta* GOLDF. 11. *Avicula contorta* PORTL. 12. *Pterophyllum jaegeri* BRONGN.

Plate 10. Index fossils of Alpine Triassic

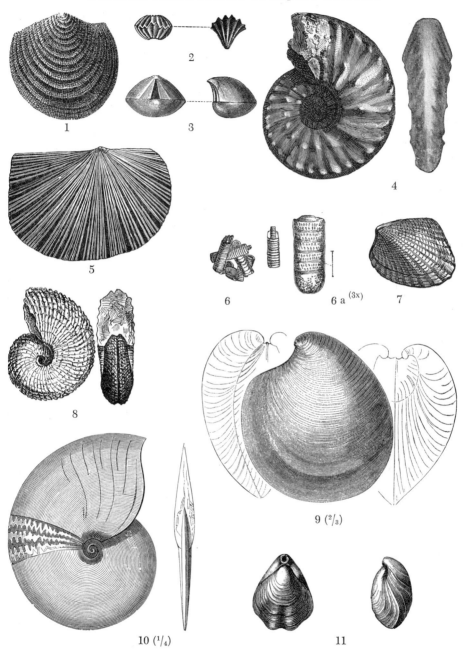

1

2

3

4

5

6   6 a $^{(3x)}$ 7

8

9 ($^2/_3$)

10 ($^1/_4$)   11

Scythian: 1. *Pseudomonotis (Claraia) clarai* EMMR. Anisian: 2. *Rhynchonella decurtata* GIRARD. 3. *Spiriferina mentzeli* DUNK. 4. *Ceratites trinodosus* MOJS. Ladinian: 5. *Daonella lommeli* WISSM. 6, 6 a. *Diplopora annulata* SCHAFH. 7. *Cardita crenata* MÜNST. 8. *Trachyceras aon* MÜNST. Norian: 9. *Megalodon scutatus* SCHAFH. 10. *Pinacoceras metternichi* HAU. Rhaetic: 11. *Terebratula gregaria* SUESS.

Supplementary Articles

C. Diener: Die marinen Reiche der Triasperiode. Denkschr. Ak. Wiss. Vienna, Math.-nat.
    Kl. 92. 1915.
E. Philippi, F. Noetling, G. v. Arthaber: Trias. Lethaea geognostica II, 1. Stuttgart
    1903—1908.
J. Pia: Grundbegriffe der Stratigraphie. Leipzig—Vienna 1930.
F. X. Schaffer: Geologie von Österreich. Vienna 1951 (s. Alpine Trias).
M. Schmidt: Die Lebewelt unserer Trias. Öhringen 1928. Supplement 1938.
R. L. Sherlock: s. p. 69.

Chapter 10.

Jurassic
Preliminary Remarks

Boundaries and classification. Initially the Jurassic deposits were exactly classified particularly in England, on the basis of W. Smith's results, by W. D. Conybeare, J. Phillips, and W. Buckland. Later, others endeavored to extend the English scheme onto the continent: H. de la Beche and E. de Beaumont in France; J. Thurmann and A. Gressly in Switzerland; and F. Hoffmann and F. A. Römer in northwest Germany, but without achieving complete clarity because of the different aspect of the rocks. It was therefore a great advance when L. v. Buch (1837) proposed a new subdivision founded on the geologic relationships in southern Germany and determined the real position of the name Jurassic introduced by A. v. Humboldt in 1795.

The Jurassic and its stages accordingly have been recognized in the main by its rocks: at first dark clay, then iron-bearing sandstones, and finally white limestones. The rocks underlying the system consist of the variegated deposits of the Triassic; toward the top widespread lacustrine beds serve as a boundary with the Cretaceous.

Distribution. In contrast to the rocks of the Triassic, which occupy a contiguous area in the central German uplands, the Jurassic is divided into two areas, a northwest German (F. Hoffmann, F. Koch, W. Dunker, F. A. Römer, W. Brauns, K. v. Seebach, Th. Brandes, and H. Salfeld) and a south German Swabian-Franconian (F. v. Alberti, F. A. Quenstedt, A. Oppel, W. Waagen, O. and E. Fraas, Th. Engel, M. Schlosser, J. F. Pompeckj, F. v. Huene, B. Hauff, F. Berckhemer, and A. Roll), which is continued in the Swiss Plateau and Folded Jura (J. Thurmann, A. Gressly, P. de Loriol, and L. Rollier). In the west European region the Jurassic occurrences of England and France belong to an originally unified basin. After the first investigators there followed H. B. Woodward, S. S. Buckman, W. D. Lang, W. Arkell, and L. F. Spath in England; W. Kilian, E. Haug, and F. Roman, in France; and E. W. Benecke and L. v. Wervecke in Lorraine. The Moscow basin is a similar large flat area of subsidence on a rigidified basement, whose contents have been investigated by S. Nikitin, A. Pavlov, and A. Borisyak. The Jurassic is widespread in the eastern and western Alps, but occupies considerably smaller areas than the Triassic. Here in more recent times V. Uhlig, F. Wähner, G. Geyer, and F. Trauth built further on the foundations created by F. v. Hauer, E. Suess, K. v. Gümbel, E. W. Benecke, C. F. Parona, K. v. Zittel, and M. Neumayr.

Principal Regions (Figs. 26—30)

Central Europe. The Jurassic sea was created by the Rhaetic transgression, which opened the Burgundian connection wider and produced a broad passageway from Tethys through eastern France to England. The epoch of the Germanic basin was thereby concluded and was followed by the episode of the later Mesozoic shelf seas, which persisted until the end of the Cretaceous. The flooding continued in the Lias and placed wide areas of Germany and almost all of France under water. Only the Ardennes-Rhenish island was left in the W and formed the margins of the German Liassic basin in common with the Vindelician-Bohemian block and the Fennoscandian-Russian northern continent. The coast lines shifted considerably in about the middle of the Jurassic. The Baltic strait created a marine connection between north Germany and inner Russia. A little later the central German land bridge extended from the Ardennes-Rhenish island to the Bohemian Massif and thus cut off northwestern Germany from the south German Jurassic Sea. Until the end of the Kimmeridgian, northwestern and northern Germany formed a part of the Baltic Straits, where northwestern and eastern European faunas met each other. On the other hand, south Germany became more closely associated with the Swiss-southern European marine region and after the subsidence of the Vindelician ridge in the Upper Malm, became a fully marginal sea to Tethys. At the end of the Jurassic a great regression took place in central Europe. South Germany became dry land. The Baltic Strait was closed. The northwest German Basin was narrowed and the water freshened, but sedimentation still continued without interruption across the Jurassic-Cretaceous boundary.

These uplifts were connected with the Kimmerian crustal movements, which took place in the youngest Jurassic and oldest Cretaceous. The Saxonic tectonic structures of northwest Germany thus originated. Volcanic activity was lacking in central Europe during the entire Jurassic.

The fauna of the central European Jurassic sea ultimately originated from Tethys and was constantly supplied from there. Ever new groups of organisms migrated in numerous waves, only to become extinct after rapid distribution and short-lived further development. Commonly the transition from the pelagic region to the shallow sea areas was connected with certain morphologic changes. The ammonites, for example, simplified their suture lines and accentuated the ornamentation of the shell. The fauna of the epicontinental seas of central and western Europe therefore contain many genera but only a few species in common with the Alps.

In *northwest Germany* the Lias is continued gradually from the Rhaetic. From the deep part of the basin, which in the coastal areas of the North sea received more than 1000 m. of mainly clay sediments, the sea shallowed toward S and E into a shoal-water girdle, which embraced in particular the Bohemian continental block.

During the Dogger in the North sea the earlier basin was uplifted. A Cimbrian land-mass emerged, on whose southern coast sand and iron oölites were deposited.

With the beginning of the Malm a general transformation took place from dark shales and brown sandstones to pale carbonate sediments. At the same time epeirogenesis was quickened, and the sedimentation of the youngest Jurassic and Lower Cretaceous was constricted to a narrow and deep trough, the Lower Saxon Basin, which extended N in front of the Rhenish Massif. From the Upper Kimmeridgian onward the salinity decreased irregularly. The Münder marl includes up to 500 m. of rock salt; the Weald, coal seams.

These incidents were accompanying phenomena of the Kimmerian orogenesis. Near the Jurassic-Cretaceous transition they first establish the present tectonic picture — the boundary of the Rhenish massif and the Harz, the graben zones of central Germany and the diapirs of northwest Germany (Figs. 27, 28). Toward the end of the Triassic the Zechstein salt, which had been buried under a load consisting of approximately 2500 m. of younger strata, began to flow. At first it collected in the core of anticlines. Finally, powerfully promoted by means of the Kimmerian mountain-building, it pushed through the overlying beds in the form of diapirs.

East Germany, the *southern Baltic areas* and *Poland* in the Liassic, as previously in the Rhaetic, formed a broad alluvial plain. It was placed under water temporarily in the lower Liassic, but for longer duration in the Upper Dogger. The Baltic strait, even if in diminished form, remained open until the Portlandian.

In *Swabia* and *Franconia* the Jurassic, especially the Liassic and Dogger, is considerably less thick than in northwest Germany. The epeirogenic subsidence of the crust proceeded more slowly and the water remained shallower. The stratigraphy shows a more pronounced subdivision and fossils are commonly more abundant. From the beginning of the Jurassic the area of the sea increased, until the break through of the Regensburg

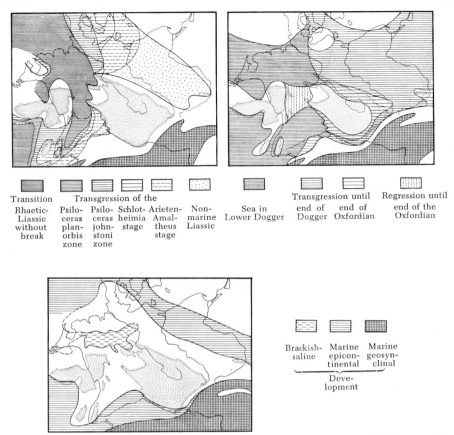

Transition	Transgression of the					Sea in	Transgression until		Regression until
Rhaetic-Liassic without break	Psilo-ceras plan-orbis zone	Psilo-ceras john-stoni zone	Schlot-heimia stage	Arieten-Amal-theus stage	Non-marine Liassic	Lower Dogger	end of Dogger	end of Oxfordian	end of the Oxfordian

Brackish-saline	Marine epicon-tinental	Marine geosyn-clinal

Deve-lopment

Fig. 26. Paleogeography of the Jurassic in central Europe. Upper left: Liassic. Upper right: Dogger and Lower Malm. Below: Lower Portland

strait, which cut off the Vindelician ridge from the Bohemian Massif. With it a tilting of the south German terrane occurred. The central German landmass emerged and during the course of the Malm increased in width toward the S, whereas in the Alpine foreland the ridge toward Tethys sank under water.

The Liassic consists in the main of blue-gray limestones and marls, which pass over into iron-oölitic sandstones toward the former coasts. As also in northwestern Germany the Liassic ε occurs as the Posidonia shale, the deposit of a sea in whose deeper parts a deficiency of oxygen existed. Near Holzmaden an abundance of splendidly preserved crinoids, fish, and marine reptiles has been collected.

The Dogger consists for the most part of ferruginous sandstones, marls, and limestones. Mineable seams of oölitic iron ore occur in Vindelician-Bohemian coastal areas in Dogger β and ε.

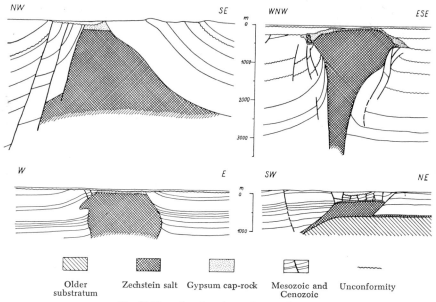

Older substratum   Zechstein salt   Gypsum cap-rock   Mesozoic and Cenozoic   Unconformity

Fig. 27. Examples of northwest German diapirs

Fig. 28. Map of the diapirs, oil and gas fields of northwest Germany (after A. Bentz)

The Malm in southern Germany, as everywhere else, brought a preponderance of pale-colored, well-bedded limestones. Reefs of siliceous
sponges that have been diagenetically dolomitized occur in the midst of
the bedded facies. The sponges proliferated as biostroms or bioherms on
the sea floor, above which they can rise 10—30 m. (Fig. 29). Sponge
growth increased during the course of time in such a way that in the
Malm ε the bedded facies was nearly displaced by the reef structures. But
soon after sponge growth terminated. Bedded rocks returned again and
filled in the bowlshaped depressions in the reef patches. One of these
fillings has become famous, that of Solnhofen in the Altmühl valley. Skeletons and in some instances the soft parts of numerous marine and non-

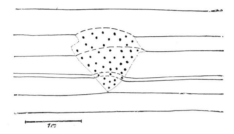

Fig. 29. Small sponge reef in the Upper Jurassic limestone. Swabian Alb (after A. Roll)

marine animals, such as jellyfish, crabs, insects, starfish, fish, reptiles, and
even the primitive bird Archaeopteryx, have been exellently preserved in
the lithographic limestone-plates.

In western and northwestern Europe with the Rhaetic transgression a
new independent area of subsidence, the Anglo-French basin, originated
in England and France. It was bounded on the E by the Ardennes-Rhenish
island and the upper Rhine ridge. The west coast was formed by a large
continental land mass which, except for Brittany, Cornwall, Wales, Ireland,
and northern Scotland, has sunk into the Atlantic Ocean. The course of
geologic events was similar to that of central Europe. A first, far-reaching
transgression took place in the Rhaetic and lower Liassic, whereas the
second, in the Middle and Upper Dogger, was of less significance. The
withdrawal of the sea which began after the Kimmeridgian and finished
at the end of the Portlandian converted large parts of the basin into dry
land again. Also here Kimmerian crustal movements followed the regression; but they were much weaker than in northwest Germany. The appearance of the rocks, in general similar to that in Germany, shows a certain
shifting of facies from S to N. Thus limestones occur first in the Liassic
of Provence, coral layers, in the Dogger of the Swiss Jura and Lorraine,
but only in the Malm are these distributed over the whole region.

The *Swiss Plateau and Folded Jura* connects the Swabian-Franconian Jurassic area with the French. The continuation of the Vindelician ridge, which is hidden under northern Switzerland, was distinguished in the Triassic. Thus it is explained that in the Jurassic the entire area is marked by a ridge facies. In the Lower Liassic this was manifested by a belated inundation which finally reached the south margin of the Jura chain beginning with the Arietites beds. Pale oölitic limestones and echinoderm limestones are common in the Dogger. The Malm is represented as in Swabia by white sponge-bearing marls and limestones. Soon however this Argovian facies was displaced by the Rauracian facies. Oölitic and coral-limestones advanced toward the Vindelician ridge from the W and NW; as in southern Germany this ridge was covered by the sea at the end of the Kimmeridgian. The Portlandian sea retreated toward the Alpine geosyncline; only in the southwestern Jura did a brackish marginal fringe persist to the beginning of the Cretaceous.

The Jurassic of *Lorraine* lay under the influence of the nearby Ardennes island in the Lias and Dogger. In the Upper Lias and Lower Dogger off the south coast of the Ardennes island the oölitic iron ores of the Minette district were deposited, especially in a bay that followed the Eifel subsidence which was characterized by a slow rate of terrigenous sedimentation. The ore formation consists of up to 12 beds generally from 1—4 m., and locally as much as 9 m. thick, which are interbedded with sandy marls. The reserves amount to 10 billion tons of ore with about 35 % Fe.

During the Triassic *France* had been an uplift area except its eastern part. The Rhaetic transgression, which proceeded from Tethys, first followed the Rhône trough, then extended between the rivers Seine and Somme to the English Channel and from there invaded England. On the other hand, it produced on the way over the Upper Rhine ridge a connection with southern Germany. In the lowest Lias the coastline was pushed back to Brittany, Aquitaine, and Provence. The Central Massif became an island. The French Jura basin, that had originated thus in place of the Gallic uplift, formed a bowl with a flat bottom. Borings demonstrate that the thickness and composition of the strata are the same in the middle part of this area as around the margin of it. At the end of the Jurassic in reciprocal succession the basin fell dry again. The western part dried up first, then the eastern part; only in the Rhône trough and Aquitaine, in the areas in front of the west Alpine and Pyrenean geosynclines, did the sea remain until the Cretaceous.

The *British Isles* in the Rhaetic and Jurassic were directly connected by the sea both with France and northwestern Germany. The Lias is in general very uniformly developed as dark clay and marly limestone. Littoral formations occur only near the borders of the Triassic basin —

in Wales, northeastern Scotland, and the Pennine ridge in the north of
England. Economically workable seams of oölitic iron are mined in the
periphery of this region. After the Lias, uplifts in Scotland and in the North
sea region (p. 86) pushed back the coast toward the S. Plant-bearing sandstones, the Deltaic series, extended into central England, where they intertongue with the bright and ferruginous calcareous sandstones, coquina-
and oölitic limestones of the Oölite series. At the end of the Dogger the
sea regained its earlier extent. The Malm here is very similar in facies
and fauna to that of northwestern Germany, but remained marine until
the Portlandian. Land and sea wrestled for control in the Purbeckian, as
the interbedding of root-bearing underclays, gypsum layers, and oyster
banks indicates. The struggle on English territory ended with a complete
freshening of the water. The sea remained during the Jurassic-Cretaceous
transition only in the northern North sea.

Alps. In contrast to the central European shelf seas, Tethys was a long-
lived sea, almost unbroken in its existence from the Triassic until the
Cretaceous. Deposits of pelagic facies, such as Aptychus- and Calpionella-
limestones, were widely distributed; the radiolarites perhaps represent true
deep-sea deposits. Like the Variscan geosyncline in the Lower Carboniferous, the Alpine geosyncline underwent an epoch of particularly deep
water. At the same time the epeirogenic mobility of the crust was more
vigorous, the classification into ridges and troughs more elaborate than in
the Triassic. Steep slopes led from the rising ridges and island chains into
the troughs and explain the abrupt juxtaposition of different facies, such
as the intercalation of breccias in bathyal sediments. In addition sequences
that contain numerous diastems, or are condensed, are widespread; in the
one individual zones are lacking, and in the other guide fossils of different
ages occur within a single bed. It seems as if currents at times kept the
sea floor nearly free of sediment. Like the Triassic, the Jurassic also elapsed
almost without orogenic phenomena. Volcanic outpourings were but little
distributed and were restricted to the deepest geosynclinal trenches.

Western Alps. The extension of the Alpine geosyncline from the eastern
into the western Mediterranean region, which we have been able to follow
since the Permian, was concluded in the Jurassic by the inclusion of the
western Alps, which until then had belonged to the Germanic region.
Facies distinctions from the rest of the Alps remained. Several ridges
which had arisen from the fingershaped splitting of the Vindelician ridge,
maintained a certain subdivision into partial troughs. The outer zone of
the western Alps is known as the Sub-Alpine-Helvetic trough. In Switzerland it was divided from the area of the folded Jura by a ridge which sank
in the Kimmeridgian, but in the French Alps it continued without demarcation into the Rhône area of subsidence. Facies and faunas are therefore

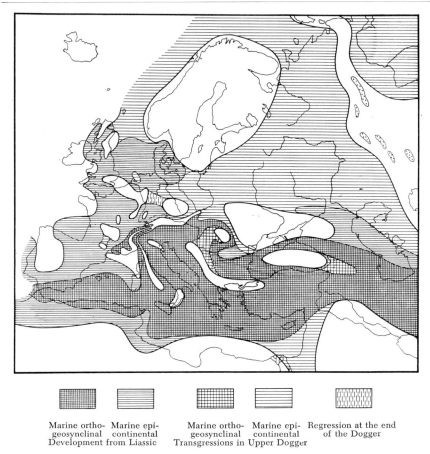

Marine ortho- Marine epi-   Marine ortho- Marine epi- Regression at the end
  geosynclinal continental   geosynclinal continental   of the Dogger
Development from Liassic   Transgressions in Upper Dogger

Fig. 30. Paleogeography of the Jurassic in Europe

particularly similar to those of the foreland. The Lias and Dogger consist
for the most part of dark sandy shales and echinoderm limestones; the
Malm, of thick, light-colored limestone that becomes marly toward the top.
Further SE one reaches the Pennine trough beyond a geanticline, the
Briançonnais axis, which particularly in the French Alps is accompanied
by breccias. In this area, which earlier had belonged to the coastal fringe
of the Muschelkalk sea (p. 74), deep-water sediments accumulated as a
result of intense subsidence. In the Lias there are the thick, uniform dark
Schistes lustrés (Bündner Schiefer), which have been transected by basic
greenstones or ophiolites, and in the Malm, radiolarites and Aptychus-
limestones.

The *eastern Alps,* in the Jurassic, as in the Triassic, display a classification of facies zones which extend from the Bohemian-Vindelician
coastal area to the open sea. On the northern margin of the Alps, especially

S of the Bohemian Massif, we find in the Lias the Gresten beds, whose coarse-grained arkoses and sandy shales with a few coal seams indicate the direct approach to a granitic coast. To the S follow finer-grained clastic and calcareous deposits, whereby the distribution of facies forms a close connection with the epeirogenesis which continued from Rhaetic time. On submarine ridges, which commonly coincide with the fronts of growing nappes, the Lias is moderately thick and consists of light-colored crinoidal-brachiopod limestones (Hierlatz limestone) which fill the crevices in the surface of the Dachstein limestone. In the troughs the Kössen beds are followed by red nodular ammonite-rich Adneth limestone, gray chert-bearing siliceous limestone or dark spotted marls and marly limestone, which are also called the Allgäu beds after the area of their principal distribution. The deposits of the Dogger in general keep to the same areas, only the facies zones have been displaced toward N the because of the continuing transgression. In the lower stages the most common rocks are spotted marls and siliceous limestones; in the higher stages, crinoidal limestones (Vils limestone) and reddish-brown cephalopod limestones (Klaus limestone). The deepest subsidence of the Alpine trough occurred in the lower Malm, as a result of which chiefly red radiolarite with an abyssal radiolarian fauna originated. The sea of the Tithonian was somewhat shallower; its northern and southern margins were fringed by coral reefs. The southern reef girdle approximately followed the line of the Hallstatt trough (p. 79) and thus permits obvious recognition of the northward migration of the east Alpine geosyncline since Triassic time.

The *central Alps* appeared as a ridge because of the occurrence of breccias in the Lias. In the Malm, and particularly in the Tithonian, they were probably fully flooded.

Southern Alps. The Triassic of the Dolomites is covered by an incomplete Jurassic succession that is only less than 100 m. thick; it is similar to the north Alpine development. More complete sections and greater thicknesses occur in the Lombardy and Vicentin Alps, but now in a southern European development, such as is widespread in the Apennines and the rest of the Mediterranean region. As a rule the Lias begins transgressively with crinoidal and dolomitic breccias. Red nodular cephalopod limestones (calcare ammonitico rosso) follow above dark siliceous limestones. They resemble the Adneth limestones of the northern Alps and are repeated in the same facies in the Upper Jurassic. In Vicentin we approach the southern shore of the Alpine geosyncline; there the influence of a landmass that is today buried under the Po Plain is indicated by the sandy, plant and bivalve-bearing Gray limestone. The greatest deepening of the sea also occurred in the southern Alps in the Lower Malm. Reddish radio-

Jura der Alpen, Ost- und Aussereuropas

Stufen	Westalpen		Nördliche Ostalpen		Südalpen		Russland	Nordamerika		Asien
	Helvetische Geos.	Penninische Geos.	Kalkalpen-nordrand	Innere Zonen der Kalkalpen	Vicentin	Lombardei	Moskauer Becken	Sierra Nevada	Felsengebirge	Vorderindien

Hangendes:

Malm:
- Purbeck / Portland — Unterkreide (Zementsteinsch)
- Kimmeridge — 400 m Quintner Kalk — 3000 m Bündner Schiefer (Schistes lustrés) — 5m Steinberger Riffkalk / 20m — Roter Tithon-flaserkalk — 500m Plassen-riffkalk — 40m Roter Tithonkalk / 50m Maiolica u. Biancone — Unterkreide (Riasanhorizont) — 10 m Wolgastufe — Unterkreide (Shasta) — Knoxville — Franciscan — Unterkreide (Neokom) — Umia
- Oxford — 5m Schilfkalk — 300m Aptychenschichten (Obersalmer Sch.) — 10m Acanthicus-kalk — 75m Radiolarit u. Aptychenschiefer — Acanthicus-kalk 20m — 35m Dunkler Ton — Mariposa — 100m Morrison — Katrol

Dogger:
- 2m Bienolith / 10m Oolithkalk — Schiefer — 50m Radiolarit — 5m Roter Malm-kalk — Bunte Radiolarite u. Posidonia alpina-Kalk — Transversarius Kalk 5m — 40m — Amador — Monte de Oro — Chari
- Echinodermen-spatkalk — 20m Klauskalk — 100m Vilser Kalk — 40m Oolith v. San Vigilio — 25m Ammonitico rosso inferiore — Thompson
- Eisensandstein 200m — 100m Mergel Posidonia alpina — Dogger-kiesel-kalk 150m — 100m Leubenstein Kalk — Graue Kalke (Noriglio Kalk) 600m — 10m Sand — Hardgrave — 100m Sundance (Ellis)

Lias:
- Opalinusschiefer 100m — 400m Flecken-mergel — 30m Adnether Kalk — Hierlatz-kalk 20m — 30m Domerator — Trail — Morrison — Paleogen
- 300m Sandiger Kieselkalk u. Schiefer — 50m Sandiger Mergel — Liäs-kiesel-kalk 100m (Allgäu-schiefer) — -500m Graue Kiesel-kalke
- Grestener Sch. 100m — Nor (Hauptdolomit) — Nor (Dachstenk) — Algonkium

Liegendes:
- Rät — Trias (Quartenschi.) krist. — Rät (Kössener Schichten) — Rät (Oberrätkalk) — Rät — Paläozoikum — Trias — Trias (Red Beds) — Rajmahal / Kota / Chaugan / Jabalpur

(Oberrätkalk)

← 90

larite is connected toward the top with the Maiolica, a fine-grained pelagic limestone, which for the most part belongs to the Lower Cretaceous.

Southern Europe and the Mediterranean region. At the western as well as the eastern ends of the Alps the partial troughs closely connected in the mountain chain forked. The Helvetic trough swings round and shallows increasingly in Provence to end at the mouth of the Rhône. The Pennine trough is continued into the Tyrrhenian sea following the apex of the former Vindelician ridge. The Bündner Schiefer correspond to the Schistes lustrés of eastern Corsica and the Argilloscisti of Liguria; both are likewise cut through by ophiolites. Lastly the south Alpine trough was connected with the Tuscan facies province of the Apuan, Tuscan, and Umbrian Apennines. The Upper Triassic transgression of Tethys toward Gibraltar was followed in the Jurassic by the prolongation of the geosyncline into the Atlantic and its extension over the chains of the Atlas in North Africa. Pelagic Portlandian occurs on the Cape Verde islands. Variegated sandstone with gypsum covers the shelf fringe of southern Morocco, Algeria, and Tunisia, in the upper part marine limestones of the Upper Dogger and Malm are intercalated.

Southeastern Europe, as we have already recognized in the Triassic (p. 80), was traversed by the Carpathian geosyncline as the continuation of the north Alpine trough, and the Dinaride geosyncline, as a continuation of the south Alpine trough. Whereas the geosynclines contain all stages of the system in pelagic facies, in part with green eruptive rocks, during the lower Jurassic the greater part of the Pannonian-Balkan-Anatolian regions between the geosynclines projected above sealevel. Liassic in the facies of the Gresten beds, in many localities with workable coal seams, is therefore widely distributed in Hungary, Transylvania, the Banat, etc. The Dogger transgression flooded considerable areas of this land mass and at the same time widened the geosynclines.

Northern and eastern Europe. Apart from the central and western European shallow sea areas a second seaway, which connected Tethys with the Arctic Ocean, existed in eastern Europe during certain parts of the Jurassic. In the lowest Jurassic it still had no outlet. The advance of the sea, which came from the Caucasus geosyncline in the Upper Lias extended only a little beyond the lower Triassic coastline. The Upper Dogger transgression was the first to create far-reaching marine connections. A wave of flooding directed itself toward the N and, as in the Permian, placed the trough W of the Urals under water. A second wave washed toward the W over the Donetz basin and joined the Baltic strait, which at the same time was extending eastward from northern Germany. After the highest level of the sea in the Oxfordian a withdrawal began. In the lower Volga stage the direct connection with central Europe was again cut off; in the upper part of this stage even the longer waterway, which led northward around Fennoscandia, was obstructed. The special position of eastern Europe for facies and fauna is also clearly displayed. The Russian Jurassic consists almost entirely of clays and glauconitic sands with beds of phosphorite nodules, which enclose beautifully preserved fossils typical of the Boreal province — Aucella, Virgatites, and Crasped-ites. Reef limestones occur only in the Donetz basin, in the opening toward the W.

The Jurassic of the **Arctic** has many features in common with that of Russia. The lowest Lias is known only in continental development. Marine middle and upper Lias occurs at only a few points in East Greenland, Spitzbergen, and the Siberian coast, yet its distribution is small compared with the areas conquered by the Dogger transgression. In the course of the Kimmeridgian the Arctic sea began to contract; fossils of the Upper Volga stage have so far been found only in Novaya Zemlya. The rocks and fossils are also similar to those of eastern Europe. Sandstones and shales with Boreal clams and ammonites predominate; sediments of chemical and organic origin are lacking.

General Features

Climate and environment. The petrographic subdivision into Black, Brown, and White Jurassic, which originated in southern Germany, is on the whole valid for almost the entire world. In many localities dark shales predominate in the lower subdivision; brown sandstones and oölitic ironstones, in the middle; and pale limestones, in the upper. There can be no doubt that this change was in the main caused climatically. Rhaetic and Liassic we have already recognized as a relatively cool moist interval. Extensive coal beds originated on the continents, and reefs were rare in the seas outside Tethys. A gradual transformation took place with the Dogger. Marine limestones of organic and inorganic origin increased in amount. Calcareous algae and corals became widespread. The Malm, as were the Silurian, Middle Devonian, Lower Carboniferous, and Middle Triassic, was a great reef-building time of the geologic past. The increasing warmth of the seas, which is indicated by this, proceeded hand in hand with an increase in the aridity of the land. Coal-formation slackened and began again only in the early Cretaceous. Sediment colors became brighter. Gypsum and salt deposits, which are almost completely lacking in the Liassic and Dogger, increased in distribution during the Malm. The processes which were responsible for the deposition of iron in oölitic form (and thereby made the Jurassic the most important post-Algonkian system for iron ore) have still not been explained.

Crustal movements and magmatism. In contrast to the geocratic Triassic, in particular after the especially pronounced withdrawal of the sea in the Rhaetic, the Jurassic was again a period of transgressions. Wide areas of the foreland were placed under water from the geosynclines. The first wave of flooding occurred in the lowest Liassic; the second, in the Upper Dogger-Oxfordian; and the third, in the Lower Portlandian:

Lower Cretaceous	
Purbeckian	Regression (northwestern and southern Germany; northwestern, western, and southwestern Europe)
Portlandian	Transgression (northwestern Germany, eastern Europe, Arctic)
∿∿∿∿∿∿∿∿∿	Late Kimmerian folding phases (northwestern Germany)
Kimmeridgian	Regression (northwestern Germany)
	Maximum spread of Jurassic seas
Oxfordian	Transgression (Bohemian Massif, Fennoscandia)
	Regression (central Germany)
Upper Dogger	Transgression (Bohemian Massif, Ardennes, eastern Germany, eastern Europe)
Middle Dogger	Transgression (Bohemian Massif, Central Massif, eastern Germany)
Lower Dogger	Regression (northern Germany, northwest Europe)
Upper Liassic	Regression (southern Baltic)
Middle Liassic	Transgression (Franconia, Paris Basin, southern Baltic, Arctic)
Lower Liassic	Transgression (central, western and northwestern Europe, southern Baltic, western Alps, Balkans)
Rhaetic	

In the highest Jurassic the great Alpine geosyncline attained its deep-sea stage which is comparable to the Lower Carboniferous of the Variscan era. The Alpine geosyncline remained nearly undisturbed by mountain-building activity. On the other hand, Kimmerian movements in the form of Saxonic fault-folds were truly widespread in the foreland plateau of central and western Europe.

Retrospect. The abundance of fossils stimulated the early investigation of the Jurassic. The methods of stratigraphic-paleontologic description, zonal classification, concept of guide fossils, and the marine biogeography of the past were developed for the most part from the deposits of this period. The climate was warm and balanced, particularly during the later stages in which pale limestones predominate. The Alpine geosyncline attained its greatest depths in connection with the general transgression, which culminated in the Malm. Shortly before the beginning of the Cretaceous the first intra-mesozoic folding occurred.

Plate 11. Lower Jurassic index fossils

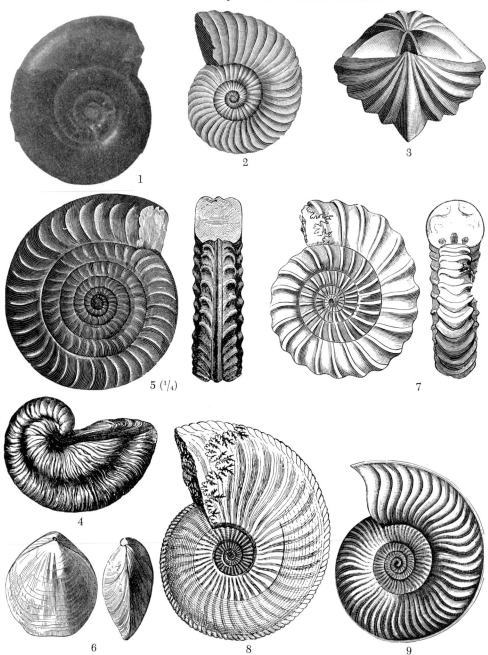

Hettangian: 1. *Psiloceras planorbe* SOW. 2. *Schlotheimia angulata* SCHLOTH. Sine-murian: 3. *Spiriferina walcotti* SOW. 4. *Liogryphaea arcuata* LAM. 5. *Arietites bucklandi* SOW. Pliensbachian: 6. *Waldheimia (Magellania) numismalis* LAM. 7. *Aegoceras (Androgynoceras) capricornu* SCHLOTH. 8. *Amaltheus margaritatus* MONTF. Toarcian: 9. *Dumortieria radians* REIN.

Plate 12. Middle Jurassic index fossils

4 ($^1/_2$)

8 ($^1/_2$)

B a j o c i a n : 1. *Trigonia navis* LAM. 2. *Leioceras opalinum* REIN. 3. *Ludwigia murchisonae* SOW.
4. *Stephanoceras humphriesianum* SOW. 5. *Parkinsonia parkinsoni* SOW. B a t h o n i a n : 6. *Rhynchonella varians* SCHLOTH. 7. *Ostrea knorri* ZIET. C a l l o v i a n : 8. *Macrocephalites macro-
cephalus* SCHLOTH. 9. *Kosmoceras ornatum* SCHLOTH.

Plate 13. Upper Jurassic index fossils

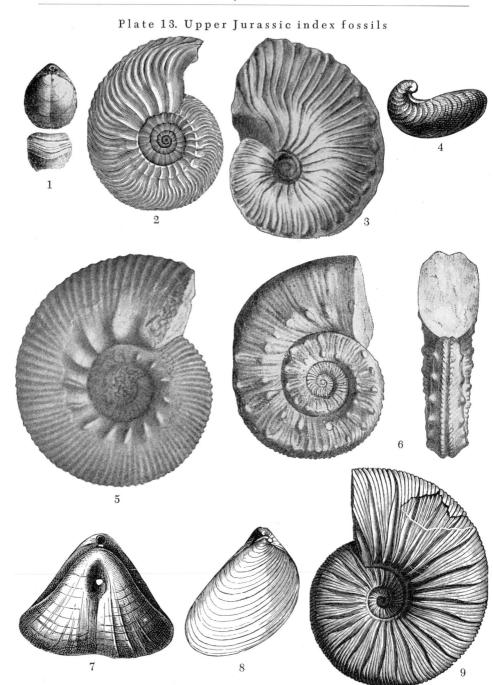

Oxfordian: 1. *Aulacothyris impressa* QU. 2. *Cardioceras cordatum* SOW. 3. *Oppelia (Taramelliceras) flexuosa* v. BUCH. Kimmeridgian: 4. *Exogyra virgula* DEFR. 5. *Aulacostephanus pseudomutabilis* DE LORIOL. 6. *Waagenia beckeri* NEUM. Portlandian—Purbeckian: 7. *Pygope diphya* COLONNA. 8. *Aucella* (= *Buchia* aut.) *fischeri* D'ORB. 9. *Virgatites virgatus* v. BUCH.

Supplementary Articles

W. J. Arkell: Jurassic Geology of the World. London 1956.

A. Bentz and others: Erdöl und Tektonik in Nordwestdeutschland. Hannover 1949 (note particularly K. Hoffmann, W. Schott, and O. Seitz).

B. Brockamp and others: Zur Entstehung deutscher Eisenerzlagerstätten. Arch. Lagerstättenforschung, H. 75. 1942.

B. Brockamp and others: Zur Paläogeographie und Bitumenführung des Posidonienschiefers im deutschen Lias: Arch. Lagerstättenforschung, H. 77. 1944.

B. Hauff: Das Holzmadenbuch. Öhringen 1953.

J. F. Pompeckj: Die Bedeutung des schwäbischen Jura für die Erdgeschichte. Stuttgart 1914.

F. A. Quenstedt: Der Jura. Tübingen 1858.

Chapter 11.

Cretaceous

Preliminary Remarks

Boundaries and classification. The designation Chalk reminds us of the times of A. G. Werner, during which the attempt was made to classify systems by lithology. After J. B. Omalius d'Halloy had given the name *Terrain crétacé* in 1822, the first investigators, W. D. Conybeare, J. Phillips, G. Mantell, and W. H. Fitton in England, A. Brongniart and G. Cuvier in France, J. F. L. Hausmann, Fr. Hoffmann, and F. A. Roemer in Germany, and J. Thurmann in Switzerland soon recognized that only by means of proper examination of the organic remains could sure progress be made. The abundance of fossils of the Cretaceous of southern France and western Switzerland gave an advantage to the geologists who were active there between 1840 and 1870: E. d'Archiac, A. Leymerie, A. d'Orbigny, H. Coquand, and E. Hébert.

Lower and Upper Cretaceous are commonly distinguished petrographically, in that the lower part consists of clays and sands, the higher part, of white chalk.

The **distribution** of the system in large parts of Europe follows that of the Jurassic. In the northern and northwestern German, south German, Anglo-Gallic, and Moscow basins the Jurassic forms the margin and bottom, whereas the Cretaceous composes the content. Besides these subsiding areas many former uplifts, such as the Bohemian Massif and the northern part of the Ardennes-Rhenish uplands, were also covered by Cretaceous deposits. In more recent time E. Beyrich, A. v. Strombeck, W. Dunker, F. Roemer, Cl. Schlüter, A. v. Koenen, E. Stolley, L. Riedel, C. A. Wicher, E. Voigt, and O. Seitz have worked in northwestern Germany; K. v. Gümbel and F. Trusheim, in southern Germany;

H. B. Geinitz, E. A. Reuss, and A. Frič, in Saxony and Bohemia; J. H. F. Umbgrove and J. Cornet in Holland and Belgium; Ch. Barrois and A. de Grossouvre, in France; A. J. Jukes-Browne, G. W. Lamplugh, F. L. Kitchin, L. F. Spath, and C. W. Wright, in England; and S. Nikitin, A. Pavlov, and A. D. Archangelski, in Russia. Also in the Alps and in southern Europe the Cretaceous corresponds with the older Mesozoic and occupies large areas, especially in the French and Swiss Alps. A. Toucas, P. Lory, W. Kilian and Ch. Jacob have been active in southern France; J. F. Pictet, E. Baumberger, and Arn. Heim, in Switzerland; and E. A. Reuss, K. v. Zittel, V. Uhlig, O. Kühn, and H. Hagn, in the eastern Alps.

Principal Regions (Figs. 31—33)

In **central Europe** the fundamental lines of Cretaceous paleogeography stem from the Upper Jurassic. The rise of the central German land bridge had divided the previously united Jurassic sea into two basins, a south German and a north German. During the course of the Malm the south German basin had become a bay on the north margin of Tethys and was revived only transiently during the Cretaceous. After the Kimmeridgian, the Lower Saxon basin in northwestern Germany had been classified apart as an area of particularly intense subsidence. It remained in existence until the end of the Lower Cretaceous. Then the differences disappeared and the North Sea basin first assumed the shape, only larger, it now bears.

The Cretaceous movements of the sea consisted of a widespread inundation, which swelled to a maximum in the Santonian-Maastrichtian; a rapid ebbing followed. At the beginning of the Lower Cretaceous the brackish-lacustrine Weald basins of northwestern Germany and the southern Baltic filled with salt water that flowed in from the northern North Sea. Then the sea began to transgress its old coastal margins. A first advance attained its greatest expansion in the Cenomanian-Turonian. The Baltic strait, the connection between western and eastern Europe, opened anew. An arm of the sea even pushed forward following the Jurassic zone of subsidence of the Regensburg strait S of the Bohemian Massif, toward southern Germany. A second wave of transgression, which led during the Maastrichtian to the widest distribution of the Cretaceous seas, followed a period of retreating coastlines in the Coniacian and lower Santonian. It was succeeded by a sharp shrinkage which continued until the transition to the Tertiary. The Baltic strait was closed. Complete sections from the Danian to the Paleocene have nowhere been found.

These developments were repeatedly accentuated by mountain-building, especially the Austrian orogeny in the Albian, the Sub-Hercynian, in the Coniacian-Santonian, and the Laramide, at the end of the Cretaceous. As in the Upper Jurassic, these took place predominantly in central and

Since Lower Cretaceous	Since Upper Cretaceous	Since Valendian	Since Aptian	Since Albian	Since Cenomanian	Regression since the beginning of the Upper Cretaceous
Marine orthogeosynclinal development		Marine epicontinental development				

Fig. 31. Paleogeography of the Cretaceous in Europe

northwestern Germany and molded more clearly the tectonic structure. As in the rest of the Mesozoic, volcanic outbursts are lacking.

As in the Jurassic, the sediments of the Cretaceous are largely marine. Even the aspect of the rocks displays a certain similarity with the Jurassic, in that the lower part of the Cretaceous consists mostly of clastic deposits, whereas the upper part consists chiefly of chemical and organic deposits. Sandstones and dark shales predominate in the Lower Cretaceous. A transformation to light-colored calcareous deposits took place with the Cenomanian, just as at the beginning of the Malm. For the most part these calcareous deposits were soft foraminiferal, bryozoan, and coccolith oozes which exist today, according to the degree of induration, as writing chalk or Pläner. Intercalated beds of flints have probably been formed by silicification of sponges. Around the landmasses which produced a lot of débris, a massive sandstone facies replaced the limestone. The light-colored thick-bedded, commonly coarse-grained Quader sandstones originated in a shallow sea, here and there even as fluvial and dune deposits.

The steady spreading of the Cretaceous sea facilitated the interchange of marine organisms. Even the Valendian fauna of northwestern Germany contains no more purely Boreal characteristics; forms from southern France and the Alps counterbalanced those from inner Russia. In the Aptian and Albian the intermingling continued; in the Upper Cretaceous it was complete. Worthy of note is a wave of migration of southern types, which temporarily colonized the central European sea in the Maastrichtian, probably as a result of a brief increase in temperature.

On the northern margin of the *Ardennes* the Cretaceous cover begins with sandy-clayey fresh-water deposits, which have been preserved in crevices and sink holes in the Carboniferous limestone. Near Bernissart, 24 complete skeletons of the dinosaur Iguanodon were found in one such. In the Upper Albian the sea invaded from the west to the Hainaut and then gradually advanced toward the E. The Cenomanian transgressed widely with the coarse-grained conglomerates of the Tourtia. Then followed the Turonian transgression, until the Campanian, after a recurrent fluctuation, reached the region of Limburg-Aachen. The Maastrichtian consists of organogenic detrital limestone, which encloses a rich warm-water fauna of reef corals, rudistids, large gastropods and echinoids, which is otherwise foreign to the central European Cretaceous seas. A sudden regression then followed; the Danian is lacking.

Hannover and Harz region. The Lower Saxon basin remained the chief area of subsidence of northwestern Germany throughout the Lower Cretaceous (Fig. 32). Its sediments were in large part conveyed from the central German landmass. At the beginning of the Cretaceous the Harz was deprived of its cover of Jurassic strata. Concretions of clay ironstone, washed out of the Jurassic shales, accumulated in drowned valleys and areas of subsidence near the former coast to form conglomerates that are locally 100 m. thick. By this means a clastic iron ore deposit with reserves of more than 1 billion tons originated near Salzgitter (Fig. 33).

The sea retreated late in the Jurassic from the southern Baltic sea region. It first encroached here again in the Valendian, and in central Poland connected, even if only temporarily, with the inner Russian sea. A through waterway of longer duration formed only in the Upper Albian, as the large Middle Cretaceous transgression allowed the Baltic strait to rise again with boundaries similar to those of the Upper Dogger.

Bohemia, Saxony, and Silesia. The Bohemian Massif was overflowed by the Upper Cretaceous transgression to a still greater degree than the

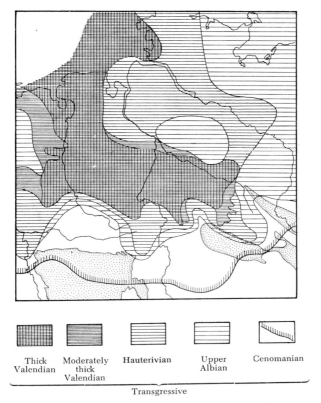

| Thick Valendian | Moderately thick Valendian | Hauterivian | Upper Albian | Cenomanian |

Transgressive

Fig. 32. Paleogeography of the Cretaceous of northwestern Germany

Ardennes-Rhenish Massif. The sea covered Saxony, Silesia, and eastern Bohemia with sharply subdivided areas; its intricate coastline already suggested some of the morphologic features of the present day. The characteristic rock of this region is Quader sandstone. Its topographically prominent escarpments are interrupted by smooth slopes which are underlain by interbedded sandy marls.

Western and northern Europe. The Portlandian uplift had left France and the British Isles almost completely dry, and the sea withdrew on the one side into the North Sea, on the other side, into the Alpine geosyncline and its immediate foreland. The Cretaceous transgression arose from both these regions. Two arms of the sea from northern England and southern France approached each other and in the Aptian united to form a unbroken channel from the North Sea to Tethys. The inundation of the Albian, Cenomanian, and Maastrichtian completely won back the territory lost in the Portlandian and in many localities transgressed beyond the Jurassic coastline. Then followed, as in central Europe, a sharp regression; Danian has not been found. Even the rock development is similar to that in central Europe. The Lower Cretaceous is composed of clays, green-sands, and siliceous shales rich in sponges (gaize); the Upper Cretaceous, of approximately 500 m. of chalky marl and chalk.

In *France* from the Upper Valendian onward, the coastline shifted again from the Rhône depression into the southern Anglo-Gallic basin, so that it followed approximately the course of the Jurassic depression between the

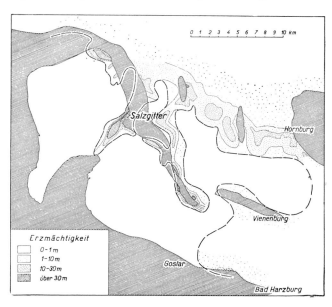

Fig. 33. Shape of the coast and thickness of clastic iron ore in the Lower Cretaceous north of the Harz (after H. Kölbel). Outcrops of pre-Cretaceous rocks shaded

rivers Seine and Somme. In the Albian the strait widened. The Cenomanian sea even covered the Paleozoic border and opened anew the strait of Poitou between Brittany and the Central Massif. In the Upper Campanian the withdrawal of the sea began; by the end of the Maastrichtian it was completed.

The *British Isles* were almost entirely dry land in the earliest Lower Cretaceous. Yorkshire alone was touched by an extension of the Arctic Ocean, whereas southern England was covered by the fresh-water lake of the Purbeckian-Weald. In the Aptian this basin was filled from the S with salt water. Finally the central English ridge was inundated and a through marine connection made. In the later Lower Cretaceous Lower Greensand, Gault, and Upper Greensand overlapped down to the Permian in southwest England, down to the older Paleozoic in the subsurface below London, so that Gault clay and glauconitic sand replace each other laterally. The Cenomanian transgression turned as in France chiefly towards the western landmass and attained its highest level with the flooding of northern Ireland and the Inner Hebrides. The English Upper Cretaceous extends to the Maastrichtian in unbroken sequence; the Danian is lacking.

Alps and southern Europe. While the Mediterranean Tethys still gained in area in the northern Alps, Pyrenees, and Atlas, the first foldings and uplifts elsewhere narrowed its extent. At the end of the Turonian, after gentle preliminary folding in the Albian, the pre-Gosauan orogeny seized the central and north eastern Alps, the Pennine zone of the western Alps and the Dinarides; the backbone of the present range was thereby created. Weaker phases followed at the end of the Upper Cretaceous. With the orogeny the epeirogenic warping of the geosynclinal floor was intensified. The troughs and ridges increased in number and amplitude. In this way crustal movements stimulated the formation of thick and uniform, predominantly clastic sequences, which have been designated as flysch. The maximum of the Cretaceous transgression in the Alpine region was attained with the latest Upper Cretaceous, when light-colored foraminiferal marls (Couches Rouges, Wang beds, Nierental beds, Scaglia) were deposited over wide areas.

The *core of the western Alps* is composed of the rocks of the Pennine trough, which together with its crystalline basement was recumbently folded and uplifted in the Upper Cretaceous. At the same time a new trough originated in front of the northern border of this mountain strip, more or less along the southern margin of the Swiss Central Massifs (Fig. 38). This trough received the foredeep deposits of the Niesen flysch and Ultra-Helvetic flysch (Wildflysch), which extend into the Tertiary. The strata consist in part of bathyal foraminiferal marls, in part of breccias, whose "exotic" constituents betray foreign origin and attain the size of blocks; perhaps these broke away from the front of advancing nappes and slid downward along the sea floor.

In the region of the *outer French and Swiss Alps* the sub-Alpine-Helvetic trough had existed since the Jurassic. In the Cretaceous also it confirmed its special position as a younger annex of the Alpine geosyncline; it remained not only free of the orogenic movements of this time but also of the flysch facies. The axis of the basin lay in the French Préalpes, the classic land of Lower Cretaceous stratigraphy. Here gray cephalopod marls 1500 m. thick were being deposited throughout the entire period. In the shelf areas which lay to the W contemporaneous shallow-water deposits originated, chiefly the pale Rudistid reef limestones and organogenic-detrital limestones of the Urgonian. During a shallowing in the Barrêmian-Aptian these shifted far into the basin. After the Maastrichtian the sea withdrew from the French Alps. In the foreland of Provence and in the geosyncline of the Pyrenees the regression began even in the Campanian; however, extensive areas of inland water were left behind which stretched toward northern Spain. The variegated brackish-lacustrine beds of the Garumnium, which extend into the Tertiary, were deposited in it. In the Helvetic part of the west Alpine trough, which comprised what is now the northern Swiss Alps, the depth of water was less than in the sub-Alpine basin. Limestone in the Urgonian facies is therefore commonly intercalated between marls, especially again in the Barrêmian and Aptian. At the Lower to Upper Cretaceous transition a certain epeirogenic unrest prevailed in the Helvetic domain. A thin cover of greensands that contains many stratigraphic gaps spread over the Schratten limestone. In the Upper Cretaceous the depth of water increased again and reached a maximum with the fine-grained foraminiferal limestones of the Seewen beds; then it diminished slowly to a final emergence of land in the Maastrichtian.

In the *northeastern Alps,* as in Switzerland, calcareous sediments were replaced by argillaceous rocks, spotted marls, siliceous limestones, and sandy marls at the Jurassic-Cretaceous transition. Mountain-building movements began early, as intercalations of coarse débris in the Hauterivian show. These movements increased in the Albian, reached a climax in the pre-Gosauan folding at the end of the Turonian, and piled up the Mesozoic rocks from the trough of the northeastern Alps into thrust sheets. The orogeny was followed by a transgression which proceeded from the northern border into the Alps and amidst fluctuations covered the northern and parts of the central eastern Alps. It left behind conglomerates, sandstones, fossiliferous Hippurites-limestones, marls, and locally even coal-bearing non-marine deposits, which are grouped together as the Gosau beds. After the sea reached its highest level in the Maastrichtian a withdrawal began. Danian is only known in restricted areas in a littoral development.

Nearly simultaneously with the first crustal movements a new trough originated between that of the northern Alps and the Helvetic trough; this trough received the rocks of the flysch zone of the Bavarian-Austrian Alpine foot-hills. Because the Alpine thrusting uprooted and transported the basin filling, the basal beds have not been found. The East Alpine flysch begins with the Barrêmian and consists of sandstone with beds of breccia, siliceous limestone, and gray and red marls, which were deposited in great thickness on a rapidly subsiding sea floor. Fossils other than "Hieroglyphs," the traces of marine bottom-dwellers, are exceedingly rare; nevertheless, one assumes that the flysch extends from the Lower Cretaceous into the older Tertiary without breaks.

In the *western Mediterranean region* the troughs and ridges had remained nearly unchanged since the Jurassic. The Mediterranean Creta-

ceous in the shallow-water regions consists predominantly of reef limestone, which in the older stages were built of Requienia, in the later stages
of Hippurites and corals. Pelagic deposits are in the Lower Cretaceous
the porcellanous limestones of the Maiolica and the Biancone, in the Upper
Cretaceous, the reddish marly limestone of the Scaglia. All these are rich
in foraminifera and other protozoa. As in the Alps, the first orogenic movements began toward the end of the Cretaceous. In the Dinarides the effects
of the pre-Gosauan orogeny were considerable. The contents of the Ligurian
trough (p. 95) were affected by the Laramide folding.

In **northern and eastern Europe** the rocks of the Volga stage and Lower
Cretaceous are closely related in distribution and composition. As in the
Upper Jurassic a sea way of varying width coccupied the pre-Uralian
depression and left behind moderately thick sands and clays with layers
of phosphorite nodules. After the constriction of the Upper Volga stage a
transgression began during the transition period and formed anew the
connection to the Arctic and to the north English sea northward around
the Fennoscandian Massif. The Moscow basin also sank under water.
During a contraction which extended from the Barrêmian to the Lower
Albian, the epeirogenic undulation veered from a N-S to a E-W direction
and created new routes to the Middle Cretaceous sea. From the Upper
Albian onward Russia and northern Germany, as in the Upper Dogger,
were connected to each other. The Upper Cretaceous sequence of eastern
Europe corresponds in facies and thickness to that of northern Germany.
Marine Danian transgresses from the Crimean-Caucasus geosyncline a
little way onto the southern margin of the Russian platform.

The Lower Cretaceous of the **Arctic,** like that of eastern Europe, is
closely linked to the Upper Jurassic. The Upper Cretaceous, on the other
hand, deviating from the familiar picture, is sharply regressive and occurs
in only a few places. In Greenland it consists of coal-bearing sandstones
and shales with a few marine layers. Worthy of note are the outcrops on
the west coast of Greenland, because they indicate the beginning separa-
tion of Greenland from the Canadian Shield.

General Features

Climate and environment. As does the Jurassic, the Cretaceous also
consists of two petrographically different parts: a lower, predominantly
clastic and an upper, mostly calcareous. The disparity in rocks may also
have been determined climatically. If, therefore, temperature and aridity
increased during the course of the Cretaceous, then it must have been
scarcely in such large amounts as in the Jurassic. The occurrence of coal-
bearing deposits in almost all stages from the Wealdian to the Danian and
the absence of noteworthy salt deposits bespeaks higher moisture. Judging

by the decrease in coral and algal reefs the sea water can only rarely have reached tropical temperatures. Indeed, the wide distribution of glauconite and the almost total absence of oölitic iron deposits signified relatively cool temperatures. One arrives at the conception of a subtropical climate with marked zonal arrangement.

Crustal movements and magmatism. During the course of the Cretaceous the first intense folding in the Alpine geosyncline began. The core zone of the Alps and Dinarides emerged from the sea as a result of the pre-Gosauan mountain-building. Further movements occurred during and after the Upper Cretaceous. As a result of this, epeirogenic warping in the geosynclinal zones became stronger. Rapidly subsiding, narrow troughs accumulated thick and uniform, prevailingly clastic deposits, which have been called flysch. These sediments henceforth fringed the growing Alpine mountains, much as previously the Carboniferous graywackes had fringed the Variscan mountains.

With the Albian began one of the largest transgressions in Earth history, and reached a first climax in the Cenomanian-Turonian, a second, in the Maastrichtian. In the Danian a rapid and incisive regression ensued.

Early Tertiary

〰〰〰〰〰Laramide folding phase (Alps, Apennines)

Danian
               World-wide regression
               Transgression (Danish Islands)

Maastrichtian
               Regression (western, central, and eastern Europe)
               Maximum spread of Cretaceous seas

Campanian
Santonian
               Transgression (northwest Germany, northern and
                  eastern Europe, western Greenland)

〰〰〰〰〰Sub-Hercynian folding phases (northwest Germany)

Coniacian
               Regression (northwestern and northern Germany,
                  Bohemia, southern Germany)
               Transgression (Eastern Alps)

〰〰〰〰〰Pre-Gosauan folding phase (Alps, Dinarides)

Turonian
               Transgression

Cenomanian
               Great transgression (western, central, and eastern
                  Europe)

〰〰〰〰〰Austrian folding phase (northwestern Germany,
                  eastern Alps)

Albian
                Regression (Arctic)
               Transgression (western, central, and eastern Europe)

Aptian
                Transgression (western, central, and eastern Europe,
                  Arctic)

Plate 14. Lower Cretaceous index fossils

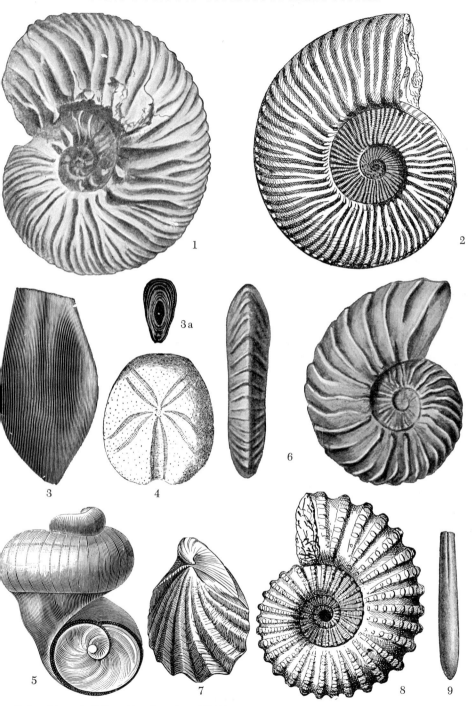

Valendian: 1. *Polyptychites keyserlingi* NEUM. & UHL. Hauterivian: 2. *Lyticoceras noricum*
SCHLOTH. 3, 3 a. *Belemnites (Duvalia) dilatatus* BLAINV. 4. *Toxaster retusus* LAM. Barrêmian:
5. *Requienia ammonia* GOLDF. Aptian: 6. *Parahoplitoides (Deshayesites) deshayesi* LEYM.
Albian: 7. *Inoceramus (Volviceramus) sulcatus* SOW. 8. *Douvilléiceras mamillatum* SCHLOTH.
9. *Belemnites (Neohibolites) minimus* LISTER.

Plate 15. Upper Cretaceous index fossils

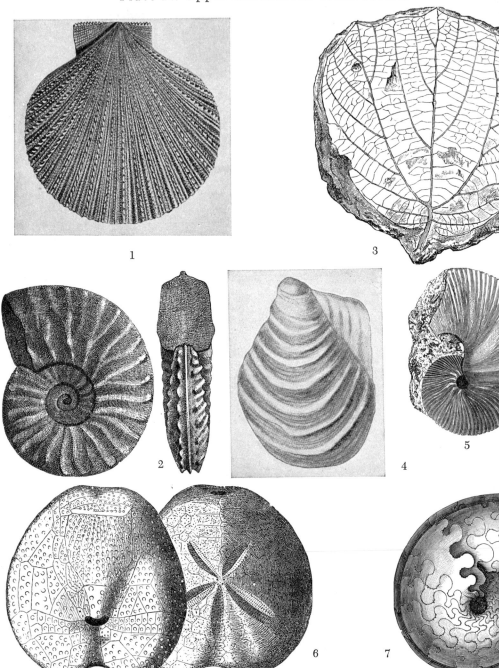

Cenomanian: 1. *Pecten (Aequipecten) asper* LAM. 2. *Schloenbachia varians* SOW. 3. *Credneria triacuminata* HAMPE. Turonian: 4. *Inoceramus lamarcki* PARK. (= *brongniarti* aut.). 5. *Scaphites geinitzi* D'ORB. 6. *Micraster cor-testudinarium* GOLDF. Coniacian: 7. *Tissotia ewaldi* v. BUCH.

Plate 16. Upper Cretaceous index fossils

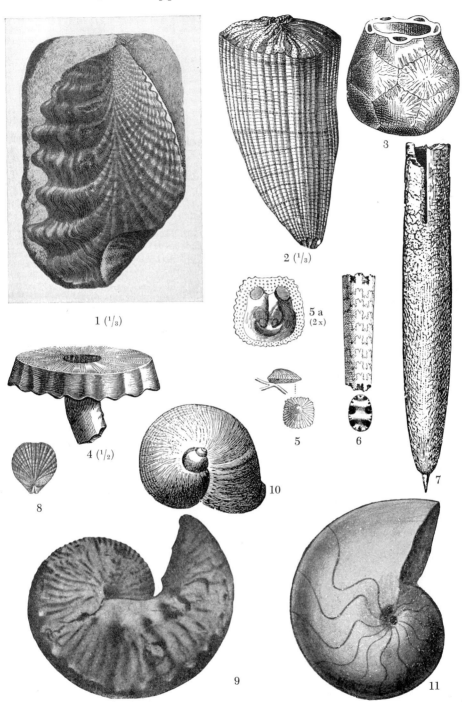

1 ($^1/_3$)

2 ($^1/_3$)

3

4 ($^1/_2$)

5 a (2 x)

5

6

7

8

10

9

11

Santonian: 1. *Inoceramus digitatus* SOW. 2. *Hippurites (Vaccinites) gosaviensis* DOUV. 3. *Marsupites testudinarius* SCHLOTH. Campanian: 4. *Coeloptychium agaricoides* GOLDF. 5, 5a. *Crania ignabergensis* RETZ. 6. *Baculites anceps* D'ORB. 7. *Belemnitella mucronata* SCHLOTH. Maastrichtian: 8. *Trigonosema pulchellum* NILSS. 9. *Scaphites (Hoploscaphites) constrictus* SOW. Danian: 10. *Lychnus matheroni* REQU. 11. *Nautilus (Hercoglossa) danicus* SCHLOTH.

Barrêmian	Regression (France, eastern Europe, Arctic)
Hauterivian	Transgression (western, central, and eastern Europe)
Valendian	Transgression (western, central, and eastern Europe, Arctic)
Malm	

Retrospect. During the Cretaceous the Alpine geosyncline was affected by the first powerful folding. Far-reaching displacements of land and sea accompanied the mountain building. The Upper Cretaceous transgression was the largest of post-Cambrian time. A sharp shrinkage followed at the transition to the Cenozoic.

Supplementary articles

A. de Grossouvre: Recherches sur la craie supérieure. Mém. expl. carte géol. France. Paris 1901.

Arn. Heim: Monographie der Churfirsten-Mattstock-Gruppe. Beitr. geol. Karte Schweiz 50. 1910—1917.

J. A. Jeletzky: Die Stratigraphie und Belemnitenfauna des Obercampan und Maastricht Westfalens, Nordwestdeutschlands und Dänemarks. Beih. Geol. Jb. 1. 1951.

E. Spengler: Versuch einer Rekonstruktion des Ablagerungsraumes der Decken der Nördlichen Kalkalpen. Jb. Geol. Bundesanst. 96, 1. 1953. 99, 1. 1956.

J. Wolburg: Schwellen und Becken im Emsland-Tektogen: Beih. Geol. Jb. 13. 1954.

Special issue on the Biostratigraphy of the Upper Cretaceous, Paläont. Z. 30. 1956.

Chapter 12.

Tertiary

Preliminary Remarks

Boundaries and classification. The name Tertiary leads us back to the beginnings of geology. G. Arduino (1759) classified the unconsolidated or slightly indurated deposits at the foot of the Upper Italian Alps as "montes tertiarii"; the abundant fossils in these deposits were similar to the organisms of the present world. In the first decade of the 19th century these rocks in Italy were more exactly described by J. B. Omalius d'Halloy. Based on this work P. Deshayes and Ch. Lyell (1830) laid the foundation for the modern classification using the proportion of species of living marine invertebrates in the fossil fauna.

The base of the Tertiary is widely marked by a stratigraphic break and a transgression from the Cretaceous system, with its different kinds of rocks and fossils. The glacial deposits of the Quaternary constitute the overlying units in many localities.

Distribution. During the course of the Tertiary the sea gradually assumed its present boundaries. Marine Tertiary deposits, therefore, are largely limited to the vicinity of present coast-lines. Only along the Alpine ranges which were arising out of the Tethys geosyncline did they penetrate more deeply into the continents.

A series of important Tertiary regions surrounds the North Sea. In the north German plain A. v. Koenen and K. Gripp continued the investigations begun by E. Beyrich about 1850. A. Dumont, H. Nyst, L. de Koninck, E. van den Broeck and M. Leriche studied the Tertiary deposits of Holland and Belgium; C. Prévost, E. Hébert, G. F. Dollfus, M. Cossman, H. Douvillé, and R. Abrard, those of the Paris basin; J. Prestwich, S. V. Wood, and Cl. Reid, those of southern England; and A. v. Koenen and J. P. J. Ravn, those of Denmark. The north German sea sent an offshoot to the Upper Rhine valley, where it left behind fossiliferous sediments, especially in the Mainz basin (F. Sandberger, F. Kinkelin, W. Wagner, and W. Wenz). The continental deposits of central Germany have been examined by E. Wüst, W. Gothan, and J. Weigelt.

The Tertiary of the Alpine mountains and surrounding regions has been studied recently in many localities, especially in southern France (Ch. Depéret, L. Doncieux, M. Cossman, and J. Boussac), Switzerland (O. Heer, K. Mayer-Eymar, H. G. Stehlin, E. Baumberger, W. Leupold, and R. Rutsch), in Swabia and Bavaria (M. Schlosser and R. Dehm), in the Vienna basin (P. Partsch, R. Hoernes, E. Suess, Th. Fuchs, and F. Schaffer), in the Pannonian basin of Hungary and its surroundings (A. Koch, M. Neumayr, and A. Winkler-Hermaden), in Italy (L. Bellardi, F. Sacco, G. de Stefanini, and M. Gignoux), and southern Russia (N. Sokolov, N. Andrussov, and A. Pavlov).

Principal Regions (Figs. 34—39)

The division of **central Europe** into two zones of subsidence, an E-W Baltic and a N-S Rhenish, had appeared in the Zechstein with the Germanic basin. Since then it had been altered, but its fundamental features, however, remained valid also for the Tertiary. During the course of the Mesozoic the axis of the Baltic depression was displaced toward the N. In the Tertiary the North Sea and adjoining parts of the north German plain became a still more pronounced area of subsidence than previously. Since the Jurassic the Rhenish depression had been crossed by the central German land bridge. In the Tertiary it was re-created though considerably narrower.

At the beginning of the Tertiary all of central Europe lay dry. The first inundation came from the N and flooded the Danish islands and the western part of north Germany in the Paleocene. The transgression of the Middle and Upper Eocene, so significant in other parts of the Earth, displaced the coastline only a little in central Europe. It brought about a widespread subsidence of the continent, however, so that henceforth the formation of lacustrine, swamp, and fluvial deposits took place in numerous continental basins, especially in central Germany. The second great wave of flooding, that of the Oligocene, following the traces of the Dogger and Albian, perhaps opened once more the Baltic strait to eastern Europe. In the Rhenish zone, too, a waterway from the North Sea to the Alpine marginal sea came into being for a short time. The regression of the Upper Oligocene cut all these connections and confined the later Tertiary seas to the North Sea basin and its immediate surroundings on the one hand, and to the southern section of the Rhenish depression, on the other.

In contrast to the Alps, where the folding of the mountains that had commenced in the Cretaceous was completed, orogenic events of only small significance were recorded in central Europe during the Tertiary. In central and northern Germany folds associated with fractures largely followed previous patterns. The tectonic development of western and southwestern Germany, however, took a very different form. In these regions during the Tertiary the epeirogenic structures were converted into orogenic ones. The depressions, which had admitted the Oligocene sea, became great grabens. The principal feature consisted of the Upper Rhine Valley graben which lies between the marginally uptilted crystalline half-horsts of the Black Forest-Odenwald and the Vosges. The graben fades out in the S, near Basel, by coming into contact with the Alpine folds. Toward the N, near Frankfurt, it forks into two shallower fracture zones and dies away penetrating into the thick young sediment filling of the north German basin.

Volcanic activity, which after a long interval that extended back to the Rotliegend (p. 60), and first revived in central European territory, was closely connected to tectonic movements. The fracture zones of west and southwest Germany were the principal sites of the outbursts. The vents and dikes are chiefly situated along NNE-striking rifts. The culmination of volcanic activity lay in the Miocene. Isolated preliminary symptoms extended back into the Upper Oligocene; aftermaths continued until the beginning of the geologic present. Size, form, and order of eruptions of individual volcanoes are of very different kinds. The eruptions of central and southern Germany belong by chemical composition to an Atlantic province, which in the Tertiary occupied large areas of central and western Europe outside the Alps. The outbursts commonly began with sodium-rich lavas of average silica content, such as trachytes or phonolites. In later stages basalts of faintly Atlantic or even Pacific chemistry attained predominance.

The Tertiary sediments in central Europe, in contrast to the Mesozoic sediments, are mostly unconsolidated and predominantly clastic. The surface of the continent was subjected to intensive weathering. Lateritic soils originated from the older Tertiary until the Lower Pliocene; the deeper parts of these soils are preserved as horizons of kaolinization. Red earths accumulated in solution holes formed on the karst surfaces of limestones. The continental sediments of the Tertiary, bright-colored fire-clays and

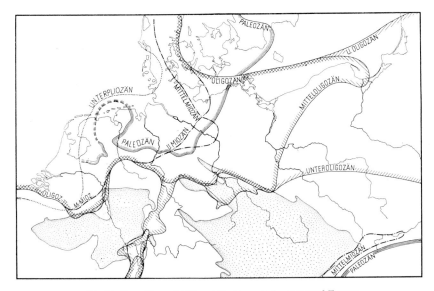

Fig. 34. Strandlines of different Tertiary epochs in central Europe

pale non-calcareous quartz sands, originated from the recycling of these residues of weathering.

Lignite occurs as intercalations within these fluvial and lacustrine deposits; these make the Tertiary second to the Carboniferous as the great coalforming period of Earth history. In consequence of their origin on a consolidated crust that was epeirogenically quiet, the Tertiary coal seams are not numerous, but instead, commonly 10—20 m., and locally 100 m. thick. Research on the coal has shown that a great number of plant communities contributed to its formation. Lakes, grass swamps, moor forests and forests alternated many times as a result of the interplay of crustal subsidence and plant growth. The composition of lignite forests altered considerably in the course of the Tertiary. In the older Tertiary evergreen broad-leaved trees and palms predominated. In the later Tertiary our indigenous deciduous trees began to spread, though the conifers still prevailed. The reserves in Germany amount to 13 billion tons of Eocene, and 45 billion tons of Upper Oligocene-Miocene lignite.

The variations in the plant cover and in rock decay illustrate the change of climate in the course of the Tertiary. After the cooler epoch of the Paleocene, the Eocene attained nearly tropical temperatures. A gradual decrease in temperature, with fluctuations, then followed and lasted until the Quaternary.

The fauna also reflected the change of climate. Among the Tertiary mammals the forest and savannah animals predominated until the Miocene. Inhabitants of the open steppe first appeared in greater number in the Pliocene with the Hipparion fauna. The molluscan faunas of the North Sea basin evidenced the decrease in temperature even earlier, because of the additional effect of geographic alterations. At the end of the Oligocene the North Sea became an appendage to the Arctic Ocean owing to the closing of the connecting passages to the south, the English Channel and the Rhenish strait. The retreat of the southern fauna therefore set in as early as the Miocene and was scarcely delayed by the short-lived reopening of the English Channel in the Middle Miocene and Lower Pliocene (Fig. 35).

Certain parts of the *Danish Islands* and *northern Germany* — that is Jutland, western Schleswig-Holstein and the Lower Elbe region — belonged throughout to the North Sea basin. Because of this they show thick continuously marine sections from the Paleocene until the Pliocene. The Moler beds contain basaltic ash layers. From the distribution of the tuff one concludes that the site of eruptions lay in the Skagerrak. The Lower Oligocene sea redeposited lumps of resin of coniferous trees from older formations in the glauconitic sand of the "Blue Earth". The exceptionally well-kept remains, especially of insects, preserved in the ensuing amber afford us a clear picture of the inhabitants of a subtropical forest of that time. In the younger Tertiary marine deposits were restricted to the immediate periphery of the North Sea.

In *Saxony and Thuringia* the Older or Sub-Hercynian lignite beds originated in the Eocene. Systematic excavations in the coal of the Geisel valley near Halle have brought to light an abundance of fossils which even preserve soft tissues and give a living picture of the conditions of that time.

The *Lower Rhenish lowland* has obviously been an old area of subsidence since the Zechstein. A large coastal swamp originated here in the Miocene protected by a bay barrier in which, during a tropical climate, the main seam, which swells up to 100 m. thick, was deposited. From the Upper Miocene onward a large river, the forerunner of the Rhine, debouched into the bay. According to the index pebbles of silicified oölites,

its source must have been located in the drainage system of the Nahe and
Mosel Rivers.

Mainz basin and Upper Rhine valley. The Upper Rhine valley depression advanced — in the older Tertiary as a geosyncline, in the younger
Tertiary as a graben — always from S to N. In the same direction the
zone of thickest sedimentation was displaced; it lay in the southern Upper
Rhine region in the older Tertiary and in the northern Upper Rhine region
in the younger Tertiary. In the Upper Oligocene the sea penetrated

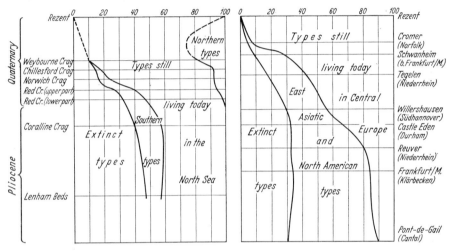

Fig. 35. Changes in the molluscan fauna of the North Sea and in the vascular plant flora of central
Europe at the end of the Tertiary (after A. M. Davis and K. Mädler)

through the Burgundian channel into this depression, perhaps from the
Rhône basin, and laid down brackish bituminous marl, with layers of rock-
salt and sylvite. The Middle Oligocene also flooded the Mainz basin, where
abundantly fossiliferous littoral deposits originated. After the Upper Oligocene regression the sea returned again for a short while in the Aquitanian,
possibly by the same route as in the older Tertiary. The first large displacements on the border faults of the graben began in the Miocene; with
these is connected the Kaiserstuhl volcano with its various Atlantic rocks.
The tectonic movements continued in the Pliocene and Quaternary.

Swabian and Franconian Alb. The Malm limestone plateau of the Alb
underwent increasing karst development as testified by sink-holes with
mammalian remains. From the end of the Oligocene on, this plateau was
deflected to the Alpine foredeep and partly flooded by the Burdigalian
sea, which incised a cliff in the Jurassic limestone up to 80 m. high that is
well preserved still today. In the Upper Miocene southern Germany was

the scene of volcanic activity; the Alb plateau was pierced by more than 180 necks.

In **western and northwestern Europe** the Anglo-Gallic basin existed since the Jurassic as a similar NNE-SSW-striking zone of subsidence that was separated from the Germanic basin by the Ardennes-Rhenish Massif and the Upper Rhine ridge. At the end of the Mesozoic the originally unified area was broken down into several separate sections. The depressions which thus originated — the London basin and the Belgian basin, the Hampshire basin and the Paris basin — were flooded repeatedly in the older Tertiary from the North Sea and Atlantic Ocean, and thereby joined the same marine region as northern Germany. Epeirogenic movements corresponded in the different basins. In the Middle to Upper Eocene the sealevel reached a first maximum; in the Lower to Middle Oligocene, a second. Then a general regression closed the history of the basins. The younger Tertiary sea, which returned in the Middle Miocene, covered only the coastal areas of Belgium, Brittany, and southern England; in the Pliocene it finally receded. The filling of the basins consists chiefly of unconsolidated sands, greensands, and clays. Indurated rocks as well as organic and chemical deposits or evaporites are rare and limited almost entirely to the Paris basin, which is the southernmost.

In *Belgium and northern France* the Montian reminds one of the Cretaceous because of its calcareous facies; it is only locally developed. The Landenian-Thanetian attained wider distribution. The fluvio-marine conglomerate of Cernay near Reims, which contains the oldest Tertiary mammalian fauna of Europe, belongs to the regressive conclusion of this stage. During the Sparnacian the sea was nearly pushed back by deltaic deposits with impure lignite. A new wave of flooding began with the Eocene. In the Cuisian the first Nummulites reached the Paris basin. The Lutetian sea brought large clams and snails as additional immigrants from the S which together with the rest of the rich fauna form the beds of the Paris Calcaire grossier. The Ludian was an arid time and the coastal areas were broken up into lagoons. The gypsum of Montmartre in Paris, which was then deposited, has been well known for its mammalian remains since the time of G. Cuvier. After the Middle Oligocene transgression the Paris basin became finally dry; the marine sand of Fontainebleau accumulated as dunes.

Southern England. The Artois axis, which separated the Belgian and Paris basins as a flat ridge, continued on the other side of the English channel as the Weald axis and divided the London basin in the lower Thames from the Hampshire basin on the Channel coast. In England, where subsidence began somewhat later than on the Continent, the dark-colored uniform London clay, like the Ypres clay in Flanders, indicates

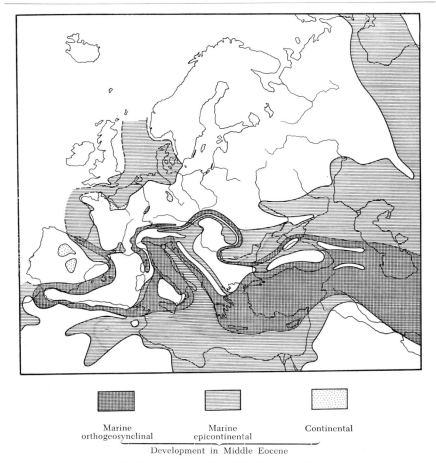

Marine   Marine   Continental
orthogeosynclinal   epicontinental

Development in Middle Eocene

Fig. 36. Paleogeography of the Older Tertiary in Europe

the greatest deepening of the sea. The higher Eocene and the Oligocene
consist for the most part of deltaic deposits, whose seaward margin oscillated with changes of sealevel. The sands and clays are colored gray in
the marine facies, but are variegated in the lacustrine-fluvial facies. The
pelecypod and bryozoan sand of the Crag, which was deposited upon
the older Tertiary along the southeast coast of England after a long break,
illustrates by its fauna the rapid climatic deterioration at the Tertiary-
Quaternary transition.

Scotland and Ireland in the older Tertiary belonged to the British-Arctic
or Thule eruption province which extended to Iceland and Greenland. In
northern Ireland and the Inner Hebrides basalt layers of high fluidity and
faintly Atlantic chemistry poured out at first and from numerous flows
built up a sheet 1000 m. thick. Then the magmatic activity focussed on
individual centers. Such an "intrusion complex" consists of silicic and

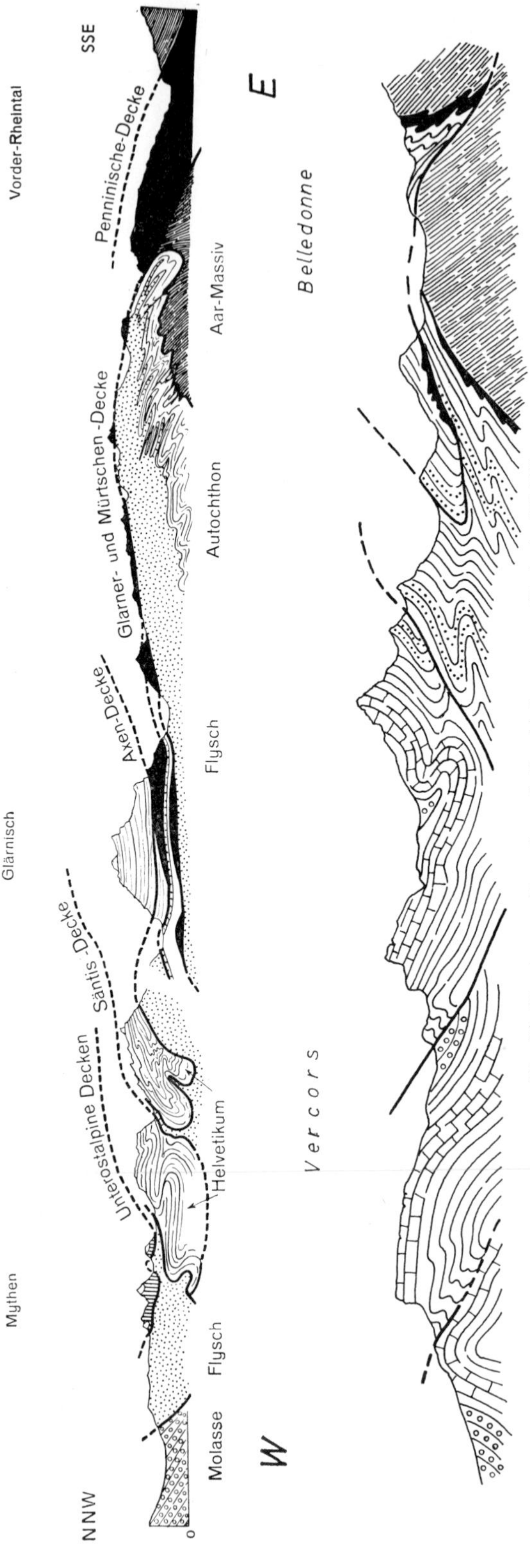

Fig. 37. Structure sections through the Alpine nappes (Scale 1 : 300,000)
Above: Recumbent folds of the Helvetic Alps (after A. Heim)
Below: Imbricate structure of the Dauphinée (after M. Gignoux)

basic plutons and dikes, which encircled a sinking caldera block. At the close of the period basaltic dike swarms originated which radiated toward the north of England.

In the history of the **Alps,** four episodes may be recognized (Fig. 37, 38).

The first episode began with the formation of the Tethys geosyncline in the late Paleozoic and ended with the pre-Gosauan folding. This folding created the core zone of the Alpine thrust mountains, which since then have remained essentially uplift regions.

The second episode corresponds to the time of the flysch, approximately from the middle of the Cretaceous until the end of the Eocene. By means of the first main folding the Mesozoic geosyncline was split into two marginal depressions, of which only the northern developed fully. The axis of this depression, which was divided into several partial troughs (flysch trough, Helvetic trough) was displaced steadily toward the foreland with further growth of the Alpine thrust-sheets. Toward the end of the older Tertiary the pressure reached a new maximum. The contents of the marginal depressions were uprooted, folded, and partly covered by the nappes of the Alps.

The third episode includes the formation, filling, and folding of the molasse foredeep. It developed from the outer zone of the Helvetic trough which had remained unfolded, and continued its migration toward the foreland. The molasse, in contrast to the purely marine flysch, originated in large part in brackish or fresh water. At the end of the Miocene, the third and last of the great Alpine folding phases compressed the contents of the molasse basin into folds which die out toward the fore-land. With this the formation of foredeeps and mountains was closed. But while the Alps grew by the incorporation of newer chains on its outer margins, disintegration already began, as in the Variscan moun-tains, in the inner parts which had been folded earlier. These disintegration processes attained significance, particularly in the eastern margin of the Alps.

In the fourth episode, in the Pliocene and Quaternary, the sea was completely expelled from the vicinity of the Alps as a result of the progres-sive uplift of the body and foreland of the mountains. From the morpho-logy — relics of old erosion surfaces, the history of valleys, and the warping of alluvial plains and terraces — one may infer an intermittent uplift and arching of the mountains which was interrupted by periods of stability, and even by times of sinking back.

Compared with that of other mountains the proportion of young erup-tive rocks in the Alps is small. The few massifs which have been reached up to now by erosion are the peri-Adriatic granites of Bergell, Adamello, the Hohe Tauern, etc., which follow the boundary between the northern and southern Alps. The time of their emplacement perhaps occurs, to judge by the appearance of andesitic tuff in the Taveyannaz sandstone, in the phase of the older Tertiary thrust movement. In the younger Tertiary vol-canic activity was still weaker and limited to a few basaltic outbursts in the periphery of the mountains.

In the *western Alps* the flysch sea occupied until the Oligocene the broad depression, which at that time still separated the Pennides (the west Alpine core zone that had been folded at the end of the Mesozoic) from the chain of the Central Massifs. In front of the steep southern coast, deposition of the wildflysch and related uniformly interbedded sequences of shales with sandstone which measure more than 1000 m. thick, continued from the Cretaceous into the Tertiary. The interspersed sedimentary and crystalline breccias, locally with slide blocks of more than 100 m.[3], must have been derived from a steeply sloped geanticline or from advancing

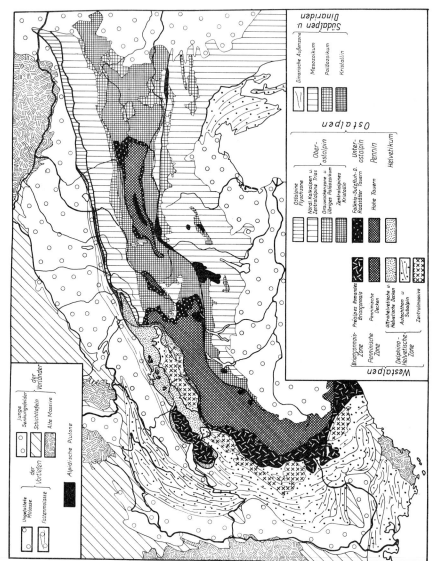

Fig. 38. General tectonic map of the Alps (Scale 1 : 5 million)

thrust sheets. Moderately thick Nummulite-limestones and greensands were deposited on the shallow northern coast, until the flysch facies also took possession of this region as a result of displacement of the axis of the Helvetic trough. The orogenesis which set in at the end of the older Tertiary transported the flysch together with its Mesozoic substratum over the Central Massifs toward the outer margins of the chain and heaped up the beds into Alpine nappes.

The *Eastern Alps*, in contrast to the western Alps, were essentially complete as a tectonic structure at the beginning of the Tertiary. They have remained land areas since then except for a temporary flooding of the Enns-Inn longitudinal valley depression in the Eocene-Oligocene. It seems that during the younger Tertiary the eastern Alps did not attain more than moderate relief owing to the reciprocal effects of uplift and denudation. The preserved remains of old alluvial coverings (Augensteine) and erosion surfaces on the present-day mountain heights show this. Especially impressive is the peneplain of the early Pliocene Rax landscape, which today rises from 1600 to more than 2500 m. from the margins toward the inner parts of the Alps. The Alps have become real mountains only since the end of the Tertiary.

Alpine foreland of Switzerland-Bavaria-Austria. In the Oligocene the molasse foredeep evolved from the Helvetic trough which had been displaced northward. The principal source of the sedimentary filling which is approximately 4000 m. thick, was the Alps; the material includes loosely cemented conglomerates (the Nagelfluh), friable feldspathic sandstones and silts. Here and there coal seams occur as geological analogues to the paralic coals of the Upper Carboniferous. Using the composition of the pebbles and heavy minerals, one can follow the gradually accelerating uplift of the Alps, interrupted by a few orogenic phases and their progressive erosion. The alluvium was deposited in the form of great fans where the streams emerged from the mountains. The finer components came to rest further away, during the regressive phases on an alluvial plain that was interspersed with lakes, and in times of flooding, in a shallow sea that was more or less brackish. Considering the direction of the transgression from E to W, the marine influence is greatest in the Austrian molasse and least, in the Swiss molasse.

On the *eastern margin of the Alps* the Alpine chains have been forced down by a transverse depression that follows the present-day Danube. This hilly region around Vienna has been named the Vienna basin — famous since early times because of the abundance of fossils. One may distinguish an outer Alpine Vienna basin that is part of the molasse foredeep from an inner Alpine Vienna basin, in which the Tertiary beds cover the sunken Alpine-Carpathian mountains which outcrop in only a few places.

The inner Alpine Vienna basin evolved from a zone of subsidence which in the younger Tertiary advanced from the Pannonian basin to the N. In the early Miocene in Styria the thick torrential débris of the Eibiswald beds accumulated in front of the steeply deflected eastern declivity of the crystalline central Alps. In the Burdigalian the sea transgressed from the south to the Drau; in the Helvetian it achieved connection with the molasse foredeep via the Vienna basin. The central Alps of Carinthia and Styria were also marginally involved in the downward movement. Here a series of limnitic basins with lignite and gravel deposits originated. The marine strait attained its greatest width in the Upper Miocene, but it began to become brackish in the Sarmatian. The deposits laid down far from the coast in the Vienna basin consist of uniform argillaceous marls, the Tegel and Schlier. In the areas near the coast, littoral conglomerates, pelecypod sands and Lithothamnian limestones (Leithakalk) originated, as did even a few small coral reefs, the northernmost ones of Miocene time. In the Pliocene the contraction and freshening of the basin continued. It became dry land by the end of the Pontian and erosion began. A series of volcanic centers followed the line of deflection of the eastern Alps toward the Pannonian depression. In the Styrian Miocene dacite, andesite, and their tuffs are widespread; the basalts are of mid-Pliocene age.

The *southern Alps and northern Apennines* have the Po plain in common as a foredeep. In the Lower Eocene the sea entered this depression from the E and in the Lower Oligocene almost reached its western tip. In the youngest Pliocene the sea withdrew again because of the discharge of sediment from the mountain rivers. The stratigraphic succession of Vicentin and Piedmont, which is abundantly fossiliferous in many localities, is exposed in a series of classic sections. Noteworthy are the marine basaltic tuffites, the Spilecco.

Southwestern Europe. Whereas the marine older Tertiary in the Aquitaine basin proceeded without break from the Cretaceous, the Pyrenean strait was interrupted near the end of the Cretaceous by the formation of the Garumnian fresh-water lake (p. 108). The marine connection was established again in the Eocene, but only for a short while, for it was ultimately obstructed by the folding of the mountains from the Oligocene onward. The Ebro basin also became dry land at about the same time; in it halite and potassium salt beds of similar age and composition to those of the Upper Rhine were left behind. The rest of the Iberian peninsula was only marginally flooded in the Cenozoic. Thick alluvial fillings accumulated in several inner basins.

Southeastern and eastern Europe. While the sea became displaced little by little from the neighborhood of the Alps during the course of the Tertiary because of broad arching movements, extensive water-filled areas of subsidence remained in existence in eastern Europe in front of and between the fold tracts. From W to E are arranged next to one another the Pannonian basin, the Black Sea basin, and the Aral-Caspian basin, which today contain the Balaton, Black Sea, Caspian, and Aral as residual lakes. The Iron Gate forms the connection between the Pannonian and the Black Sea basin and the Manytsch strait northward from the Caucasus to the Aral-Caspian basins. In the Middle Miocene this chain of basins had

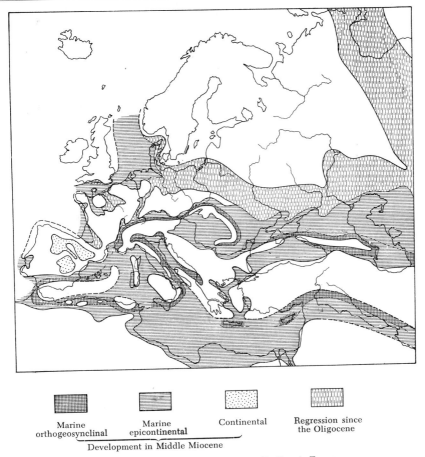

Marine
orthogeosynclinal   Marine
                           epicontinental   Continental   Regression since
                                                                        the Oligocene
Development in Middle Miocene

Fig. 39. Paleogeography of the younger Tertiary in Europe

three outlets to the open sea: through the Rhône valley, the Bosphorus, and via Mesopotamia to the Persian Gulf. The blocking of the western outlet led to a loss of salinity in the Sarmatian, which progressed from W to E. The sealing also of both other straits in the Pliocene completed the freshening of the water.

Around the periphery of the Mediterranean, as in the Alps, the first thrust movements took place in the Mesozoic geosynclinal areas toward the end of the Cretaceous; the formation of flysch foredeeps followed this. Further folding in the course of the Tertiary created the present mountain tracts. The Mediterranean Tertiary is therefore on the whole regressive; particularly intense was the constriction in the Pontian. The connection to the Atlantic Ocean in the Miocene passed over the marginal depressions of the Betic Cordillera in southern Spain, and over the Rif in Morocco. The straits of Gibraltar first opened in the younger Pliocene. The Mediterranean in its present form is a young creation, as proved by the distribution of plants and animals in its marginal lands and islands. A landmass existed in the Tyrrhenian Sea until the beginning of the Pliocene. The dismemberment and flooding of the Aegean was first completed in the Quaternary.

General Features

Climate and environment can be determined in the Tertiary far more exactly than in the older systems. The deposits are excellently preserved and contain organisms closely related to those of the present day. Climatically the Tertiary was governed by a nearly steady decrease in temperature. The most intense warming occurred, after the somewhat cooler epoch of the Paleocene, in the Middle Eocene. The general cooling began with the Oligocene. In the Older Tertiary palm trees thrived near London; at the end of the Miocene they disappeared from central Germany; at the beginning of the Pliocene, from southern Germany. At the same time the northern limit of coral reefs withdrew toward the equator. In the Eocene the London basin preserved the northernmost examples; in the Miocene, the Vienna basin. Inorganic climatic indicators tell the same story. Allitic weathering ceased; in western Germany the Lower Pliocene basalts bear the youngest kaolin and bauxite soils. In contrast to the nearly continuous decline of temperature, the amount of precipitation fluctuated. Times of salt deposition (Upper Eocene, younger Miocene) alternated with maxima of coal formation (Middle Eocene, older Miocene). Seasons of the year were clearly established in the Tertiary. This is proved by the lamination of lacustrine sediments, growth rings of tree trunks, as well as by scales and auditory ossicles of fish.

Crustal movements and magmatism. During the later Cretaceous the core zones of the Alpine mountain chains of Europe had been folded. The Tertiary includes the last act of the compression and the first stages of the disintegration of the young orogenes. The Pyrenean phase, the second great orogenesis of the Alps after the pre-Gosauan phase, completed the Decken structures that had begun in the Cretaceous. The Attian-Rhodanian phases folded the molasse and closed the period of mountain-building in Europe. The Mediterranean remains as a remnant geosyncline from Tethys.

The displacement of the coastline fitted into the rhythm of the folding. Two maxima of flooding in the Middle Eocene and Middle Oligocene followed the far-reaching regression that occurred at the transition of Cretaceous to Tertiary. In the Neogene the arching movements that proceeded from the young mountains began to encroach more intensely on the foreland. The sea withdrew gradually; the peak of geocraty was reached in the Quaternary.

Pleistocene

Pliocene

Regression (North Sea basin, Mediterranean)
Transgression (western North Sea basin, Mediterranean)

∿∿∿∿∿∿∿Attian and Rhodanian phases of folding (French Pré-Alpes, Swiss folded Jura, north Alpine molasse foredeep)

Regression (North Sea basin, molasse foredeep)

Miocene

Transgression (molasse foredeep, North Africa)

Regression (central and northwest Europe, molasse foredeep, southern Russia)

Oligocene

Second maximum spread of Tertiary seas

Transgression (central, western, and northwestern Europe; Alps; Mediterranean region; Africa)

∿∿∿∿ ∿∿∿∿Pyrenean phase of folding (Swiss Alps, Eastern Alps, Pyrenees)

Regression (northwest Europe, Alps, North Africa)

Eocene

First maximum spread of Tertiary seas

Transgression (western and northwest Europe, Alps, Mediterranean region, North Africa)

Regression (Belgian and Paris basins)

Paleocene

Transgression (Denmark, north Germany, western and northwest Europe, Swiss Alps, southern Russia)

∿∿∿∿∿∿∿∿Laramide phase of folding

Danian

In connection with the crustal movements eruptive activity showed a lively increase over the whole of Europe. The Eocene and Miocene were truly the times of the most intense magmatic activity. Pacific granites intruded into the young fold chains; only a small part of these seem to have been uncovered by erosion. Enormous basalt outpourings of weakly Atlantic or undetermined affinity spread over the consolidated masses.

Retrospect. The Tertiary was the time of a gradual approach to the conditions of the present. As a result of the small distinction between the coastlines then and now, predominantly continental sediments and littoral deposits of shallow seas have been left to us. In spite of progressive cooling, lignites were formed almost throughout the whole Tertiary and make it next to the Carboniferous the second greatest coal-system of Earth history. Halite and potassium salts were deposited in drier epochs, but in smaller amounts than in the Permian.

The lively tectonic events remind us of the occurrences at the end of the Paleozoic. Like the Variscan mountains the young Alpine chains increased in width by annexation of the deposits in their marginal depressions. Vigorous plutonic and volcanic processes accompanied the folding. In the

Plate 17. Tertiary index fossils

Paleocene: 1. *Venericardia pectuncularis* LAM. 2. *Ostrea bellovacina* LAM. Eocene: 3. *Nummulites distans* PUSCH. 4. *Cerithium serratum* BRONGN. 5. *Velates schmiedeli* CHEMN. Oligocene: 6. *Charonia* (= *Tritonium* aut.) *flandrica* KON. 7. *Turris* (= *Pleurotoma* aut.) *belgica* NYST. 8. *Ostrea ventilabrum* GOLDF. 9. *Nuculana* (= *Leda* aut.) *deshayesiana* DUCH. 10. *Glycymeris* (= *Pectunculus* aut.) *obovata* LAM.

Plate 18. Tertiary index fossils

Miocene: 1. *Ancilla glandiformis* LAM. 2. *Fusinus* (= *Fusus* aut.) *longirostris* BROCCHI. 3. *Conus ponderosus* BROCCHI 4. *Turritella turris* BAST. 5. *Cassis (Semicassis) saburon* LAM. 6. *Mactra (Ervilia) podolica* EICHW. 7. *Pecten solarium* LAM. Pliocene: 8 *Fusinus (Neptunea) antiquus* L. 9. *Melanopsis hastata* NEUM. 10. *Viviparus hörnesi* NEUM. 11. *Cardium (Agricardium) acardo* DESH. 12. *Congeria subglobosa* PARTSCH. 13. *Arca (Anadara) diluvii* LAM.

later Tertiary a general uplift forced back the sea and caused the continents
to emerge above sealevel with their present contours.

Supplementary Articles

F. Bettenstädt: Paläogeographie des nordwestdeutschen Tertiär. Erdöl und Tektonik,
p. 143, Hannover 1949.

H. Füchtbauer: Transport und Sedimentation in der westlichen Alpenvorlandsmolasse.
Heidelb. Beitr. Min. Petr. 4, 26. 1954.

F. Kirchheimer: Die Laubgewächse der Braunkohlenzeit. Halle 1957.

K. Lemcke u. a.: Geologische und sedimentpetrographische Untersuchungen im West-
teil der ungefalteten Molasse des süddeutschen Alpenvorlandes. Beih. Geol. Jb.
11. 1953.

A. Papp and E. Thenius: Vösendorf, ein Lebensbild aus dem Pannon des Wiener
Beckens. Mitt. Geol. Ges. Vienna 46, 1. 1953.

H. W. Quitzow: Altersbeziehungen in der jüngeren Braunkohlenformation nördlich der
Mittelgebirge. Geol. Jb. 68, 227. 1953.

F. X. Schaffer: Geologie von Österreich. Vienna 1951 (cf. Ostabdachung der Zentral-
alpen, Wiener Becken, Molassezone).

J. Tercier: Le Flysch et la sédimentation alpine. Ecl. Geol. Helv. 40, 164. 1947.

J. Weigelt u. a.: Researches into the lignite deposits of the Geisel Valley near Halle. Nova
Acta Leopoldina since 1 (1932).

W. Wenz: Das Mainzer Becken und seine Randgebiete. Heidelberg 1921.

Die Niederrheinische Braunkohlenformation. Fortschr. Geol. Rheinld. u. Westf. 1/2.
1958.

Report of the Symposium of the Tertiary. Ber. Geol. Ges. DDR 3, 85. 1958.

Chapter 13.

Quaternary

Preliminary Remarks

Boundaries and classification. In 1829, J. Desnoyers took the latest part
of the Tertiary, which extends into the present, and named it the Quaternary. The designations of the stages of the Quaternary correspond with
those Lyell had applied to the Tertiary. The significance of the Quaternary
deposits offered considerable difficulty at first. True, as early as the beginning of the last century a few investigators (J. Venetz, K. Schimper, and
L. Agassiz) concluded from the distribution of polished bedrock and far-
transported "erratic blocks" that previously there had been a considerably
greater extension of the present glaciers. But no one thought to explain the
young unconsolidated formations in the plains of northern Europe in a
similar way. L. v. Buch and Ch. Lyell persisted in the notion that these
deposits had been produced by mudflows and floating icebergs from the N.
Only after W. Buckland (1840) in England and A. Torell (1875) on the
Muschelkalk near Berlin first found glacial scratches did the continental ice

theory ultimately triumph over the drift theory. Around 1880 A. Penck and
K. Keilhack pointed to the occurrence of fossiliferous deposits that were
interbedded between the successive till sheets. This testified to repeated
advances and melting of the glacier; that is, a multiple alternation of ice
ages and interglacial ages, or in general terms, of cold periods and warm
periods. One therefore also names the Quaternary the Ice Age and fixes
its beginning by the occurrence of the first intense climatic deterioration.

Distribution. In area the Quaternary is the most widespread of all
systems. The lowlands of the continents are covered almost without
interruption by Pleistocene or Holocene deposits. The Quaternary sediments that were deposited on the floor of the sea are accessible to us only
in a few places because of the moderate extent of recent displacements of
the coastline. Our knowledge, therefore, is limited chiefly to continental
deposits.

The previously glaciated areas are especially important. The northern
European glaciated region includes Scandinavia, the Baltic, Russia, nor-
thern and central Germany, together with the British Isles; it has been
investigated by geologists from Germany (K. Keilhack, C. A. Weber,
E. Wüst, W. Soergel, R. Grahmann, K. Gripp, P. Woldstedt, and F. Firbas),
Denmark (V. Madsen, V. Milthers, and K. Jessen), Sweden (A. G. Nathorst,
R. Sernander, H. Munthe, G. de Geer, and L. v. Post), Finland (M. Sauramo), England (J. Geikie, Cl. Reid) and Russia (G. Mirtschink, W. Krokos,
W. Dokturovski, and S. A. Yakovlev). In addition to these continental ice
fields there were a great number of glaciated mountains. The most important are the Alps, whose investigation was chiefly divided among the
Germans (A. Penck), Austrians (E. Brückner, O. Ampferer, R. v. Klebels-
berg) and Swiss (Alb. Heim). Quaternary research, apart from the glaciated
regions, has also recently produced important results, particularly around
the periphery of the Mediterranean Sea (M. Gignoux, A. C. Blanc, F. E.
Zeuner, M. Pfannenstiel).

Principal Regions (Fig. 40—45)

Northern Europe and northern Germany had been closely related geo-
logically since the Late Paleozoic, as the Fennoscandian uplift and the
Baltic depression. In the Quaternary they formed a new relationship as
the source- and melting area of the north European continental glacier,
respectively. During the course of the Pleistocene extensive firn fields were
repeatedly formed in the mountains of Scandinavia; these began to flow
as glaciers and covered northern Germany to the foot of the uplands in the
form of a continuous ice-sheet. The continental ice ground down the rocky
framework of northern Europe and transported the débris toward the S
where in the southern Baltic and in the north German plain it was depo-

sited when the ice melted in a layer 50—100 m. thick. The ice ages
alternated with warm periods during which the glacier dwindled approximately to present size. The last warm period, the Holocene, extends into
the present.

The deposits of the ice ages are composed about equally of material
formed by the glaciers and by meltwater. Till consists of a mixture of rock
types from the N in all grain sizes from the finest silt to erratic blocks of
more than a meter in diameter. From the fabric of the till — for example
the orientation of the long axis of boulders — conclusions may be drawn
concerning the direction of the ice movement. In view of the rarity of
glacial striations in northern Germany, this method is important. Also,
erratics which originated from a narrowly bounded source area, the so-
called indicator boulders, have been useful for determining direction.
Because each glacier shows its own distinctive flow pattern, counts of
indicator stones likewise have become stratigraphic tools. Meltwater divided the unsorted till according to grain sizes — blocks, gravel, sand and
silt — and transported them, the smaller particles being carried greater
distances. Laminated clay, which came to rest in the Baltic Sea at the end
of the Ice Age, has been used as a basis for calculating absolute time in
the most recent geologic past because of its seasonal stratification.

In contrast to the older systems, whose deposits have been disclosed
for the most part only in cross-section the upper surface of the Quaternary
deposits lies open before our eyes. The glacial morphology shows that the
scenery of a formerly glaciated area can reveal the behavior of a continental glacier. Morphology has also become an important stratigraphic
tool. The succesion of terminal moraines indicates a series of halts in the
melting period. Naturally, the more completely preserved the surface
morphology, the later it must have been uncovered by the melting ice. The
morphologic boundary line between the young and the old moraine regions
in the north German plain is especially striking. It separates the youthful
morainic topography, uneven and pitted with lakes, from the smoothed
erosion landscape of the older Pleistocene which is devoid of lakes.

The interglacial and Holocene deposits are like those of the present,
for they originated under very similar conditions. Fluvial, lacustrine and
bog deposits, such as gravel and sand, gyttja and peat, are widespread;
in the North Sea and Baltic, mud and shell sands were deposited. Research
into their pollen, diatoms, and foraminifera content permit deeper in-
sights into the environmental and climatic relationships than is possible
with the much rarer macrofossils.

Quaternary crustal movements followed inherited lines and accordingly,
viewed in the large, consist of further uplifting of Fennoscandia and a
continued sinking of the Baltic strait. At the beginning of the Quaternary

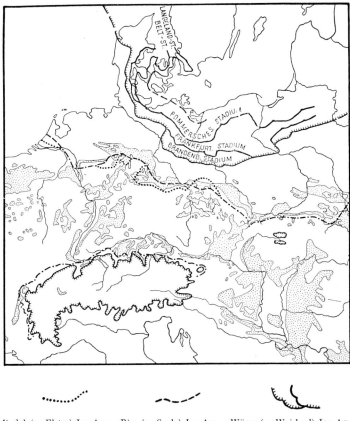

Mindel (= Elster) Ice Age   Riss (= Saale) Ice Age   Würm (= Weichsel) Ice Age
and re-advances

Fig. 40. Glacial boundaries and distribution of loess (stippled) in central Europe
(after R. Grahmann and P. Woldstedt)

north Germany was dry land; today the base of the Pleistocene lies up to
more than 100 m. below sealevel, and reaches its greatest depth where
Tertiary subsidence was most marked (Fig. 41). The warping apparently
took place without faulting. The north German Quaternary strata, to be
sure, are commonly folded and thrusted, but these phenomena are to be
explained by glacial push, not as tectonic disturbances. Evidence of volcanic activity is entirely lacking.

The stratigraphy of the Quaternary proceeds from the fact that in
northern Germany till and glacio-fluvial deposits are repeatedly interbedded with one another in beds 10—30 m. thick. Glacial advances and
ice-free intervals therefore alternated with each other several times. Many
of the glacial retreats were only brief episodes; these are called inter-
stadials. A few, however, lasted longer and were accompanied by decisive

climatic improvements, as the fossils indicate. These are the interglacials, which divide the Ice Age into individual glaciations. On this basis it is possible to distinguish 3 glaciations in northern Europe.

At the beginning of the *Old Pleistocene* the growth of land that prevailed through the entire younger Tertiary reached a maximum. The Baltic basin lay dry, and also in the North Sea basin the sea had retreated far from the present coast. Deposits from this continental interval are pre-

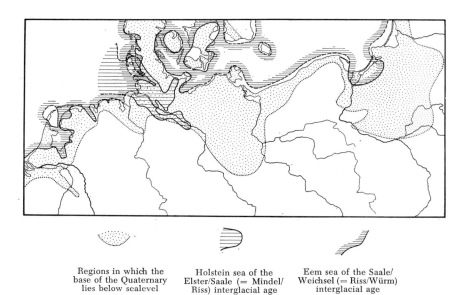

| Regions in which the base of the Quaternary lies below sealevel | Holstein sea of the Elster/Saale (= Mindel/ Riss) interglacial age | Eem sea of the Saale/ Weichsel (= Riss/Würm) interglacial age |

Fig. 41. Interglacial seas and Quaternary areas of subsidence in northern Germany

served only in a few areas of subsidence, for example, in the Rhine-Maas delta. Here fluvial sands and muds intertongue with brackish and marine deposits. Their fossil content permits recognition of the gradual extinction of the stragglers of the Tertiary fauna and flora as the climate repeatedly deteriorated. Moraines from these first cold intervals have not been recognized; perhaps the glaciers therefore did not advance beyond northern Europe.

The ice reached the uplands of central Germany for the first time in the *Middle Pleistocene*, in the Elster glacial age. After its disappearance the Holstein sea transgressed to the mouth of the Elbe River, perhaps even as far as the western Baltic, and brought along a Boreal molluscan fauna. The fluvial deposits of the Paludina beds of the subsurface beneath Berlin are of the same age. The climate of this warm period was more continental, and perhaps somewhat cooler than at present.

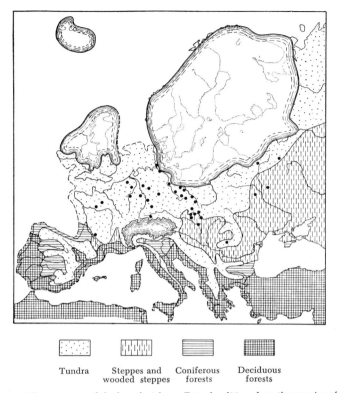

Tundra   Steppes and   Coniferous   Deciduous
              wooded steppes forests   forests

Fig. 42. Europe at the maximum of the last glacial age. Dots: localities where the remains of Pleistocene
musk oxen have been found (after J. Büdel, W. Soergel, and M. Gromova)

Young Pleistocene. The Saale glaciation on the whole attained the same distribution as its predecessor. The climatic curve of the Saale-Weichsel interglacial age was also similar to that of the preceding warm interval, only the summers were more oceanic and 2° C warmer than today. The transgression of the Eem sea entered via the English Channel, flooded the North Sea as well as the Baltic, and established a temporary connection with the White Sea via a strait that crossed Karelia. The Eem fauna shows a number of southwest European molluscs, which signifies a warmer water temperature than exists at present in northern Europe.

In the Weichsel glacial age the glaciated surface was considerably smaller than before, and offered a picture of a Baltic glacier whose firn masses were distributed in a tongue-shaped pattern over the plains east of the Elbe River (Fig. 42). The time of maximum glaciation was followed by Late Glacial melting period, whose subdivisions are indicated by end moraine ridges in the lands around the southern Baltic (Fig. 40). Finally the ice broke into two parts (bipartition) and melted back to the position of the modern ice-caps of the Scandinavian mountains.

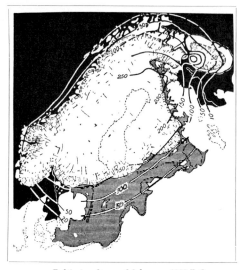

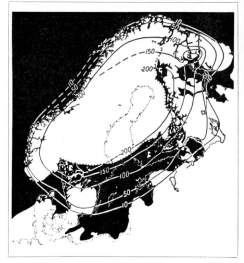

Baltic ice-dammed lake, ca. 8200 B.C.
The ice margin lay at the Fennoscandian
end moraine

Yoldia sea, ca. 7700 B.C.

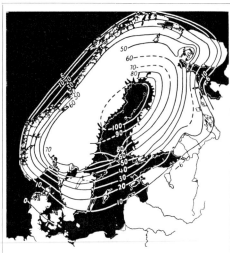

Ancylus lake, ca. 6000 B.C.

Littorina sea, ca. 5000 B.C.

Fig. 43. Northern Europe in Late Glacial and Holocene time (after M. Sauramo)
The lines illustrate the uplift of Fennoscandia that has occurred since the individual stages indicated

At the end of the last glacial age, as in the interglacial ages, a transgression began and became visible as the disappearing ice released southern Sweden and the Baltic region. The Kattegat became a marine bay
and in the southern Baltic, a meltwater basin, the Baltic ice-dammed lake,
originated (Fig. 43).

With the retreat of the ice margin from the central Swedish moraine — by agreement the beginning of the *Holocene* — a wide strait opened up over central Sweden about 10,000 years ago, through which the salt water of the Yoldia sea with its Arctic fauna entered the Baltic basin. Simultaneously the core of Fennoscandia began to rise and to warp into the shape of a shield, a process that has continued until the present day with decreasing velocity (Fig. 43, 44). The uplift forced the sea out of central Sweden. The Baltic again became isolated from the sea and freshened to

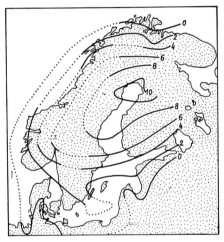

Fig. 44. Present-day rate of uplift of Fennoscandia in mm/year
(after B. Gutenberg)

the Ancylus lake, whose waters flowed out through the Belt. Two thousand years later the sea gained renewed entrance via the Danish straits and thereby introduced the Littorina episode. In this interval the salt content of the Holocene Baltic sea reached to its highest maximum but because of a gradual constriction of its connecting passages, sank to its present state in the Lymnaea and Mya episodes.

The North Sea which lay dry as far as the Dogger Bank at the transition Pleistocene-Holocene, on the other hand, experienced only a single large inundation. It set in as the Flandrian transgression and in dying away reached the present shore of the Heligoland bay as the Dunkirk transgression. In the southern Baltic region the displacement of the coastline has probably ceased, but in the North Sea coastal subsidence has continued decreasingly until the present day.

The changes of climate since the last glacial maximum can be read from the history of the forests by means of pollen analysis (Fig. 45). At the beginning of the Late Glacial time, the north German plains that had been freed from the ice were colonized by a treeless tundra with mosses,

Jungpleistozän und Holozän

Abt. u. Stufen	Absolute Chronologie	Nordeuropäisches Inlandeis Rückzugstadien	Ostsee-stadien	Oslo Strandterr.	Klima u. Pflanzenkleid in Mittel-europa			Kulturen Norddeutsch Mittel- und land Westeuropa	Fauna in Mittel-u. Nordeuropa	Alpines Vereisungsgeb. Rückzugstadien Schneegrenz	Nordamerikan. Inlandeis Rückzugsstadien
					Klimastufen	Wälder	Pollenzonen v. Firbas				
(Postglazial) Holozän	+1000 Chr.Geb. −1000 −2000 −3000 −4000 −5000 −6000 −7000 −8000 −9000 −10 000	Bipartition −6840 −8150 Mittelschwedisch-süd/innl. Stadium −8800 Südschwed. St. Langeland-St. Pommersches St. Frankfurter St. Brandenburger St.	Mya Lymnaea Litorina −5100 Ancylus −7250 Yoldia Baltischer Eissee	Mya (10m) Ostrea (+22m) Trivia (+47m) Tapes (+70m) Mactra (+95m) Pholas (+142m) Litorina (+15m) Portlandia (10m) Mytilus (+121m)	Nach-wärmezeit Spät Mittl. Frühe Warmezeit Sub-arktische Zeit Arktische Zeit	Wirtschaftsforste Buche Eiche u. Fichte Eiche mit Buche u. Fichte Eichen-mischwald Kiefer u. Eichenmischwald Kiefer u. Hasel Kiefer u. Birke Birke u. Kiefer Tundra Birke Baumlose Tundra Birke u. Kiefer Tundra Kiefer Fichte Hainbuche Eichenmischwald	X IX VIII VII VI V IV III II Ib Ia Ic	Geschichtliche Zeit −500 Eisenzeit −1800 Bronzezeit Neolithikum Ertebölle Campigny Magle-mose Tarde-nois Azil Lyngby-Ahrensburg Hamburg Magda-len Solutré Font Robert Gravette Aurignac s.s. Châtelperron Aurignac Mousterien und Levallois	Waldfauna in Deutschland +Mammut in Sibirien +Ren in Dänemark +Ren in Deutschland +Mammut, Höhlenbär; Nashorn in Deutschland	+1600 Fernau-St. ? Egesen-Stadium Spätkristr. Rückgang der alpinen Gletscher Daun-Gschnitz-Schlern-Stadium Ammersee-St. Singener-St. Schlieren-St. Schaffhausener-(Killwangener-)St. Göttweiger Interstadial Altwürm Riß/Würm-Interglazial	−50m −100m +300m Cochrane Valders Two Creeks Cary Tazewell Iowa Farmdale Sidney Alt-Wisconsin Sangamon

Jungpleistozän: Spätwürm / Mittelwürm / Frühwürm / Eem (ca 15 000, ca 25 000, ca 50 000, ca 100 000)

herbs, dwarf birches, and polar willows. Then the trees migrated into it, and for the first time in the short-lived warm phases of the Bölling- and Alleröd interstadial, birch and pine formed sparser woodlands. These were almost entirely destroyed by the climatic setback that coincided with the halting of the ice margin at the central Swedish end moraine. But in the pre-Boreal they returned again, only with the continued warming they were supplanted by more demanding deciduous trees — hazel, oak, elm, linden. The Holocene climatic optimum coincided with the highest level of the Littorina transgression; summer temperatures then were 2—3° C warmer than now. Afterward, the weather again became somewhat moister and cooler, and beech, spruce, and fir spread further.

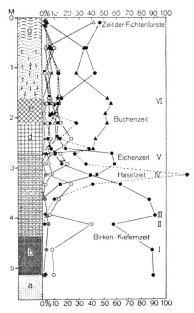

Fig. 45. Pollen diagram from the Feder-
see region, Upper Swabia
(after K. Bertsch)

The sum of the tree pollen = 100%; hazel pollen is shown separately from the total proportion of other pollen. After mineral muds (a. laminated clay, b. clay mud, c. marl) follow organic muds (d. + e. peat mud), finally after the conversion to land, moor peats (f. Scheuchzeria peat, g. Sphagnum peat).
  I. = Alleröd time
 II. = youngest Dryas time
III. = pine time

Man followed the disappearing ice. The first hunters and fishermen still met with mammoths and reindeer in northern Germany. In the Alleröd they reached Scandinavia. In the Neolithic age primitive agriculturalists migrated into the land; with their clearing of the forests man's interference with the natural plant cover began.

Central and southern Germany, Belgium and France in the Pleistocene belonged essentially in the non-glaciated area between the north European and Alpine glaciation regions. Glacial deposits are rare here; only the highest peaks carried small local glaciers and firn fields. Periglacial deposits covered correspondingly larger areas; these originated under the influence of the glacial climate. Thanks to the large variety and rich fossil content of the deposits, the unglaciated regions provide in many respects more favorable circumstances for investigation of the stratigraphy and environmental conditions of the Quaternary than the glaciated regions themselves.

The Quaternary can be divided into three parts on the basis of its mammalian faunas. In the youngest Tertiary and oldest Quaternary the animal world experienced a progressive impoverishment. Many of the warm-loving animals of the forest and savannah which were adapted to a warmer climate — such as tapirs, antelopes, Hipparion, Mastodon, sabre-toothed tigers, and apes — migrated away or died. In their place at the beginning of the Quaternary appeared the inhabitants of the steppe that were adjusted to the colder climate: horses, bison, elk, and giant deer; these were later joined by reindeer and mammoths. In the Middle- and Young Pleistocene a balance prevailed, as two faunas, which are named after the leading elephant types, alternated with each other according to the changes in climate. The glacial community or Primigenius-fauna, was composed of inhabitants of the steppes and tundra: the mammoth, horse, bison, reindeer, woolly rhinoceros, and a host of small rodents. The inter-glacial, or Antiquus-fauna, consisted of animals of the forest: the forest elephants, smooth-haired rhinoceros, deer, and boar. The predatory animals, bears, lions, and hyenas, were not closely tied to the climate. A last turning point lay at the end of the Pleistocene. Mammoths and cave bears died out; the reindeer receded toward the N before the present-day forest fauna.

Man entered early into central European territory; the oldest remains that have been found to date are the lower jaw of Mauer near Heidelberg. Skeletons and tools from later times are more abundant and are well known from many open land- and cave settlements.

The Quaternary flora, as does the mammalian fauna, shows a picture of increasing impoverishment and repeated alternations between forest and steppe. The forests of the warmer times resembled those of today, but spruce, fir, and hornbeam were more widely distributed, whereas the red beech was nearly lacking. During the glaciations central Europe belonged to the treeless tundra. The northern boundary of the dense forests lay S of the Alps (Fig. 42).

The far-reaching displacement of the animal- and plant zones provides us a concept of the degree of the Quaternary changes in climate. During the interglacial times the weather differed little from that of the present day. The glacial climate, on the other hand, was continental and severe, and the summers particularly were short and cool. The yearly average temperature lay 8° C and more below that of today. The precipitation also was doubtless somewhat smaller than at present.

Frost and wind found a broad field under these conditions and pro-duced a considerable cover of periglacial deposits. Permafrost extended to considerable depths; in its uppermost layers, cryoturbation, solifluction and patterned ground originated because of the alternation of freezing and thawing. The amount of rubble produced by frost-action created a transportation problem for the rivers, which could not wash away all the material because of the smaller amounts of water that were available during the glacial intervals. The valleys therefore filled with gravel masses, which were totally or partially cleaned out again during the interglacial times when rainfall was more abundant. Aggradation and erosion alternated, and to the extent that no tectonic movements intervened, they were parallel to the changes of climate during the Pleistocene. By this means it is possible to classify the stages of the fluvial terraces and to connect them to glaciations. The wind had free play on the glacial outwash plains, fluvial terraces, and solifluction deposits, which were without a protective plant cover. It lifted off the finer grained particles, which were continually being produced by frost action and deposited the transported material again after a sorting into grain-size fractions as blown sand or loess. The loess is the most important of these deposits; it blankets considerable areas with thickness on the average of 1—3 m. Loess, like the terraces, is of glacial origin. In the interglacial times wind action stopped and humid weathering created a zone of loam, which allows us to make a subdivision of the loess profiles. Apart from other sediments, cave deposits originated, and even these weakly reflect the climatic changes. During glacial ages frost rubble accumulated on the cave floors. In the warm periods groundwater promoted the formation of calcareous sinter. Traces of the inhabitants, such as artifacts of men and bone-breccias of cave bears became incorporated into these.

Tectonic movements, continued from the Tertiary into the Quaternary with decreasing intensity. They led to the evolution of the present landscape by means of a renewal of erosion, and can be read from the displacement of Pliocene erosion surfaces, deepening of valleys, and warping of fluvial terraces.

Volcanic activity had two centers, the Rhenish graben zones of western Germany and the Central Massif of France, where the sites of eruptions are likewise localized on N-S fractures. The last eruptions in both areas occurred in the late Würm ice age.

Alps and Alpine foreland. In contrast to the continental glaciers of northern Europe, the Pleistocene glaciation of the Alps was displayed as mountain glaciation. The valley glaciers in the Alps were amalgamated over passes and low ridges into a network of ice streams and extended their tongues far into the foreland. Only the highest mountain crests projected above the firn fields.

In almost all localities, therefore the face of the Alps bears the features of glacial morphology, which have remoulded the morphologic forms that originated during the Tertiary. Only the proportion of glacial influence in the creation of the present-day morphology is not clear. Especially in dispute, is in what respects the trough-like valleys with their characteristic cross section and step-like long profile as well as the cirques with their abrupt walls are the results of rivers or glaciers. Today one is inclined to evaluate in this respect the morphologic effects of rivers as being greater than the abrasion of glaciers, and to think that the ice cover in general more conserved than destroyed the pre-Quaternary features of the Alps.

In the *northern Alpine foreland* a zone of subsidence corresponding to the Baltic strait of north Germany was lacking. The Pleistocene deposits therefore attain comparatively small thicknesses of approximately 20 m. Everywhere the old land surface comes through; it guided the movement of the glacier. The moraine content of the ice was almost completely washed out during the melting of the ice. Meltwater deposits, are, accordingly much more abundant than till. In the Bavarian-Swiss Alpine foreland the valley glaciers which emerged from the mountains united with their neighbors to form large piedmont glaciers which pushed forward up to 100 km. toward the N. Toward the eastern and western ends of the Alps the ice stream network became less intricate and broke down finally into single glaciers whose tongues ended in the mountains. Each ice stream carved out a depression that is girdled by end moraines, a terminal basin, which today either shelters a lake or has been filled by silt or bog deposits. Meltwater excavated a passage through the moraine-wall into the ice-free foreland and there deposited its sediment cargo on wide gravel plains. Each longer halt of the glacier produced such a glacial series, consisting of terminal basins and moraines, and gravel fields. In the course of time meltwater cut ever more deeply into these, so that the gravel surfaces have been cut into a series of terraces, the highest of which is connected to the oldest stillstand position, and the lowest with the youngest stillstand position.

On the *southern margin of the Alps* ice streams, too, pushed forward into the foreland, but they remained separate from each other. The gravel fields from these united in the region of subsidence marked by the Po Valley plain to form a widespread depositional mass that is as much as 2000 m. thick. In northern Italy the furthest advances of both the last glaciations lay much closer together than on the northern margin of the Alps. The end moraines amalgamated therefore to form enormous amphitheaters that are as much as 250 m. high, such like those which run around the southern end of lakes Garda, Iseo, Como, and Lugano. The regionally different intensity of glaciation of the Alps is explained by the fact that the moisture-bearing winds during the Pleistocene came chiefly from the Atlantic Ocean, just as they do today. The glacial snowline therefore rose parallel to the present one, from W to E and from the margins toward the interior of the mountains.

Tectonic movements during the younger Pliocene and oldest Pleistocene consisted of a powerful uplift, as indicated by the deepening of valleys that were cut in the Tertiary erosion surfaces. The Alps thereby became real mountains. The warping was accompanied by faulting; Lake Constance subsided along Quaternary faults. In more recent time tectonic quiet has prevailed; the terraces of the last glacial age are nowhere markedly disturbed. Volcanic activity has died out since the Tertiary except for a small Holocene pumice outburst in the Ötz valley.

The *stratigraphy of the Alpine Quaternary* is chiefly based on the gravel terraces and their interfingering with end moraine ridges. In the Alpine foreland four large gravel-field systems that are separated by erosion intervals can be recognized. The highest and oldest rests as cemented Nagelfluh sheets on the watersheds. The youngest gravels line the present-day river valleys as terraces. Accordingly one may distinguish four glacial ages; as in northern Europe, they were preceeded by glacial advances of lesser extent.

So far, the oldest cold periods, designated the Donau glacial ages, have been evidenced only by means of floral changes in the older Pleistocene fresh-water deposits of northern Italy, and by a few occurrences of high gravel terraces in upper Bavaria. The Günz glacial age is also known essentially from its meltwater deposits.

In the Mindel and Riss glacial ages the Alps underwent their most intense glaciation. Both glaciations had about the same extent, as shown by their terminal moraines. During the intervening Mindel/Riss or Great interglacial age the south Alpine gravel plains were deeply weathered to a red-brown loam, the Ferretto. On the north side of the Inn valley, near Innsbruck, a talus deposit known as the Hötting breccia formed. The plant cover resembled that of the present day, but the Pontian Alpine rose and the wild grape bespeak a milder and moister climate than at present.

The Riss/Würm interglacial age was of shorter duration. Yet judged on the basis of the plant content of the Swiss Schiefer coals, it seems to have been just as warm as its predecessors. In any case, the glaciers had melted back so far that Paleolithic men first entered the Alps at this time, and caves at altitudes of 2400 m. could be inhabited. During the Würm glacial age, as in northern Europe, the distribution of glaciers was smaller than before. The individual ice streams remained more separated. The young moraine ridges, terminal basins and gravel terraces are well preserved and in a step-like arrangement, corresponding to the main recessional stages of the north German-Baltic moraines. During melting, many landslides into the valley occurred owing to the release of undercut slopes; the largest of these was the Flims landslide in the Hinterrhein, whose volume was 12 km^3. The postglacial climate- and colonization history proceeded as in northern Europe; but in the higher areas spruce predominated over beech. In the Holocene warm period the snowline was raised approximately 300—400 m. above its present-day position and the mountains were nearly ice-free. A new growth of the glaciers followed, the apex of which was reached in the years between 1600 and 1850; since then they have been in continual retreat.

The Quaternary of the **British Isles** is thinner, but otherwise similar to the north German deposits. The older Pleistocene, as in Holland, was divided into several cold ages. In the marine shell-sand of the Crag are found scattered erratic boulders that can be traced to the calving glaciers of Norway. Meanwhile the North Sea began its withdrawal. In the section at Norfolk, the Crag is overlain by the mud and peat of a united Rhine-Maas-Thames delta, the Cromer Forest Bed. The actual Ice Age begins in the British Isles, as in northern Europe, with the Mindel glaciation. The continental glacier radiated chiefly from the Scottish Highlands, but to a lesser extent from the Northern Ireland uplands. Two principal streams advanced from the areas of ice supply toward the S, a western tongue through the Irish Sea and an eastern tongue through the North Sea. The latter was temporarily deflected by the Scandinavian ice that filled the North Sea. Both older glacial advances reached nearly to the River Thames; the sharply lobate margin of the youngest advance remained further to the N. Marine intercalations in the glacial deposits and elevated marine strand-terraces indicate that the British Isles passed through several periods of uplift and subsidence. They find especially clear expression in the English Channel. The marine strait that had been closed since the Pliocene was opened temporarily in the Eem interglacial and ultimately from Littorina time onward. Prehistoric man was able to colonize early this area linked to the continent; his first crude stone implements are found in the Cromer Forest Bed, perhaps even in the Crag.

Eastern Europe. The continental glacier, whose margin extended almost in a straight line from southern England to the northern Carpathians, became lobate in eastern Europe; its large tongues and re-entrants were adapted to the tectonic subdivision of the Russian platform into depressions and uplifts. The chief region of supply for the glaciers lay in northern Scandinavia, with smaller centers in Kola, Novaya Zemlya and the northern Urals. In eastern Europe, also, one can distinguish three glaciations, with perhaps one previous weaker one; the middle of the three was the most significant. During the intervening warmer periods the polar sea flooded the coast of western Siberia and northern Russia. At least the last interglacial Boreal transgression formed a connection with the Eem sea of the Baltic via Karelia. In southern Russia, the moraines were replaced by a wide girdle of periglacial deposits and finally by the sediments of the Black Sea-Caspian depression. The Ukraine loess forms a layer that is 10—20 m. thick on the average. The loess is composed of five stages that have been separated from each other by buried soils, the middle of which corresponds to the Riss glacial age.

In the **Mediterranean lands** the coasts are fringed by a series of step-like terraces, of which the highest lies 200 m. above, and the lowest more than 100 m. below present sealevel. Displacements of the strandline and climatic changes were bound together in such a way that transgressions coincide with warm and regressions with cold periods. The fauna of the Calabrian stage confirms a notable cooling of the water compared with that of the Pliocene by the first appearance of northern molluscs. The non-marine deposits of Villafranca are of the same age. Their fossil content demonstrates that the subtropical forests of the Tertiary were displaced by temperate coniferous and deciduous forests, in which a Quaternary mammalian fauna characterized by the elephant, horse, deer, and cattle, lived with the last Mastodon and Hipparion. The Strombus fauna which indicates the Tyrrhenian and Monastirian, contains strangers from the West African coast, which require a higher water temperature than at present. In these two warmer periods the Mediterranean and Red Sea were connected for the last time across the Suez isthmus. Salt water also flowed into the Black Sea basin which had become brackish since the younger Tertiary. During the last glacial age the sealevel lay 100 m. below the present coast, as drowned valleys and karst topography, fluvial gravels, and peat deposits demonstrate. The Black Sea became freshened again and its water overflowed into the Mediterranean via a Bosphorus-Dardanelles river. The postglacial transgression first created the present conditions.

General Features

Climate and environment. The most important phenomenon of the Quaternary is glaciation. It was one of the most significant in Earth history and formed the lowest point on the temperature curve that had been falling since the Eocene (p. 128). Particularly in the northern hemisphere where large landmasses surrounding the pole offered favorable prerequisites, continental ice sheets spread.

The phenomena can be recognized by a repeated depression of the snowline of approximately 600—1200 m. that was clearly simultaneous throughout the world. The Quaternary glaciation consisted, so to speak, of an enormous enlargement of present-day glaciers. The question as to what proportion lower temperatures and what proportion increased precipitation influenced the growth of the ice is today answered on the side of cooling

as the primary factor. During the ice ages the mean annual temperature
fell 4—8° C on the continents, 6—7° C in the surface waters of the oceans.
The cooling brought an increase in precipitation with it, as the steeper
temperature gradient between the pole and equator accelerated atmospheric circulation.

The cause of the Ice Age must have been comprehensive, considering
the generality of the phenomena and its widespread previous history which
extended back into the Tertiary. Today some are inclined to attribute the
Ice Age to a diminution of solar radiation, whose fluctuations were sharpened and increased by terrestrial factors. Without doubt an epoch of
extensive uplift and growth of land masses, as happened in the younger
Tertiary-Quaternary, had offered especially favorable conditions for the
development of glaciers. Then continental glaciers and thoroughly cooled
polar ocean basins inclined to stability and even survived warmer intervals.
An example is the present-day polar ice caps, which although holdovers
from the Ice Age, still deeply influence atmospheric circulation and
climate. An opposite theory — that the oceans held the key to Pleistocene
climatic changes — has, however, also been advanced.

Crustal movements and magmatism. In spite of its short duration the
Quaternary was an epoch of considerable paleogeographic changes:

Holocene	Regression (Northern Baltic, British Isles)
	Transgression (Baltic, North Sea, British Isles)
Würm glacial age	Regression (Baltic, North Sea, English Channel, Arctic Russia, Mediterranean)
Riss/Würm interglacial	Transgression (Baltic, North Sea, English Channel, Arctic Russia, Mediterranean)
Riss glacial age	Regression (North Sea, Mediterranean)
Mindel/Riss interglacial	Transgression (North Sea, Mediterranean)
Günz glacial age	Regression (Mediterranean)
Mindel glacial age	Transgression (Mediterranean)
Günz/Mindel interglacial	Regression (North Sea)
Villafranchian	Regression (North Sea, Mediterranean)
Pliocene	

A cyclical recurrence of the events is conspicuous. Several possibilities
must be kept in mind to explain their causes in the Quaternary which
diverged from the older periods. The first is epeirogenesis which proceeded
throughout, even in the Ice Age. The second is isostatic processes, which
means a yielding of the Earth's crust under the weight of growing ice
masses. By their growth continental glaciers bent down the crust and
allowed it to rise up again after their disappearance. Probably readjust-
ment proceeded slowly owing to the plastic state of the zone of compen-

Plate 19. Quaternary index fossils

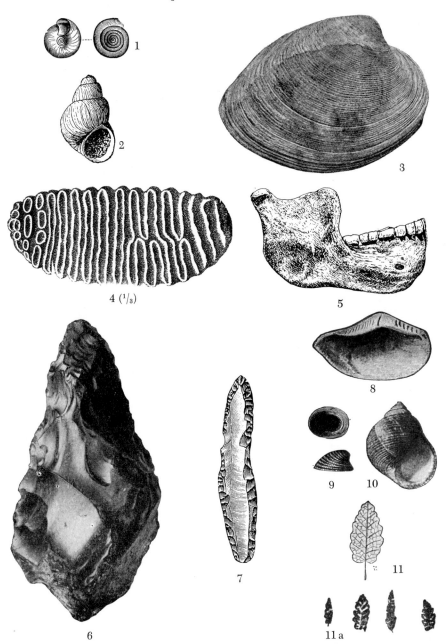

4 ($^1/_3$)

Pleistocene: 1. *Fruticicola hispida* L.   2. *Viviparus* (= *Paludina* aut.) *diluvianus* KUNTH.
3. *Paphia aurea* GMEL. (= *Tapes senescens* DÖD.).   4. *Elephas* (*Mammonteus*) *primigenius* BLUMENB.
5. *Homo* (*Palaeanthropus*) *heidelbergensis* SCHOET.   6. Hand-axe Acheulian. 7. Blade, Aurignacian.
Holocene: 8. *Yoldia* (*Portlandia*) *arctica* GRAY. 9. *Ancylus fluviatilis* L. 10. *Littorina litorea* L.
11. *Dryas octopetala* L., Alpine variety, 11 a. Arctic variety.

sation. The third is the growth and melting of the glaciers, whose growth confined considerable amounts of water on the land and whose release must have caused eustatic movements of sealevel.

Orogenesis in central Europe was limited to posthumous movements of small magnitude. The circumference of the Mediterranean was the site of more intense Quaternary mountain building. Here crustal warping accompanied by earthquakes is still in process at present in many localities. Quaternary colvanism was of small intensity and occurred essentially in the areas where it is still active today.

Retrospect. The decrease in temperature that had persisted since the Tertiary led in the Quaternary to an enormous growth of glaciers. The Pleistocene is divided into a series of cold and warm intervals. As a result of glaciation clastic deposits of glacial and periglacial origin in the form of moraines, gravel, and loess, were distributed over large parts of the continents.

The cause of the Quaternary climatic fluctuations is not yet clarified. Its aftermaths in the form of polar ice caps and lower sea water temperatures have not yet disappeared. It is therefore possible to suppose that the Ice Age has still not come to an end and that we are at present living in an interglacial time.

Supplementary Articles

M. Ewing, and W. L. Donn: A Theory of Ice Ages. Science, 123, 1061.

F. Firbas: Waldgeschichte Mitteleuropas. Jena 1949—1952.

R. Grahmann: Urgeschichte der Menschheit. Stuttgart 1956.

G. Heberer: Neue Ergebnisse der menschlichen Abstammungslehre. Göttingen 1951.

K. P. Holdhaus: Die Spuren der Eiszeit in der Tierwelt Europas. Abh. Zool.-Bot. Ges. Vienna 18. 1954.

P. Woldstedt: Das Eiszeitalter. Stuttgart since 1954.

F. E. Zeuner: The Pleistocene Period. London 1958.

Eiszeitalter und Gegenwart. Since 1951.

Quartär. Since 1938.

Quaternaria. Since 1954.

Transactions of the International Association for Quaternary Research. Since 1928.

Climate number of the Geol. Rundschau 34, 307 ff. 1944.

Chapter 14.

The Development of the European Continent

Precambrian. A crystalline basement underlies the sedimentary cover everywhere in Europe. It can be shown, however, especially in the middle and southern part of the continent, that metamorphism has also affected Paleozoic and even Mesozoic strata. Undoubted Precambrian sequences have been recognized to be widely distributed only in northern and eastern Europe. In addition, there are a few scattered smaller areas, as for example the Bohemian Massif, where fossiliferous Cambrian rocks similarly place an upper limit on the age of the underlying rocks.

In those localities where detailed investigations have been made — Sweden, Finland, Karelia, Kola, the Ukraine, and Scotland, the Precambrian has correspondingly been subdivided into three parts, which are separated by two great unconformities. Absolute age determinations, which have been undertaken on a wider scale only lately, have raised doubts about individual points of this subdivision, but have confirmed it as a whole. In contrast to Canada and Africa, age figures greater than 2,000 million years have till now remarkably seldom been attained. Therefore, the core of Europe may be younger than that of the other continents. Many lithological similarities exist with the oldest masses in other parts of the Earth. Volcanogenic and clastic deposits predominated in the oldest times, whereas carbonate rocks first occur in greater thickness in the younger eras. As in the rest of the world, the Precambrian of northern and eastern Europe is distinguished by banded siliceous iron formations. Red non-marine clastic rocks are widespread in the younger Algonkian.

Apart from older orogenies, we find a great Middle Algonkian mountain-building episode in the tectonic structure of northern and eastern Europe. The folds which thus originated cross the Swedish-Finnish basement diagonally in a NW-SE direction and bend toward the south in eastern Europe (Ukraine). The building of the core of the European mainland was completed with this phase. Known as the Baltic-Russian Shield, or Fennosarmatia, it includes the lowlands of Sweden, Finland, and Russia together with the Baltic Sea. Jointly with the Hebridian Massif, now almost completely sunken, and the Greenland-Canadian Shield, Fennosarmatia may be considered to have constituted a larger unit, the North Atlantic primeval craton.

A period of continental conditions which lasted until the beginning of the Cambrian followed the mountain-building. Parts of Fennosarmatia, such as Finland, Karelia, and the Ukraine, have even remained above sealevel until today. The red non-marine deposits of the latest Algonkian

Fig. 46. Tectonic structure of Europe (after H. Stille)

Fennosarmatia Laurentia Africa	} in Precambrian era	
Pal-Europe	in Caledonian era	} rigidified into cratons
Meso-Europe Meso-Africa	} in Variscan era	
Neo-Europe	in Alpine era	

of northern and eastern Europe form a contrast with the central and southern part of the continent, where predominantly marine sediments underlie the Cambrian. The distinction between the cratonal north and geosynclinal south which characterizes the geologic history of Europe until the Cenozoic, was therefore established at a very early time.

In the Late Algonkian, the Canadian-Greenland Shield was separated from the Baltic-Russian Shield by a zone of subsidence which extended from Scotland via the mountains of Norway toward Spitzbergen. Thus the Caledonian geosyncline came into existence and was filled with thick deposits which range in age from the highest Algonkian to the lowest Cambrian. Rocks of similar age have been recognized from the Urals. The present-day boundary of Fennosarmatia and the building of the great Paleozoic geosynclines therefore extend back to the Precambrian.

Cambrian. Sedimentation was widely discontinuous between the Precambrian and the Paleozoic. The oldest trilobite zones of the Lower Cambrian thus far have been found only in Morocco and southern Spain; the Holmia stage is the first that is recognized over all of Europe. The special position of southern Europe was thereby manifested, again, and further emphasized biogeographically by the occurrence of Pacific trilobites. The significance of the Mediterranean as part of the Tethys oceanic belt became clear for the first time.

In the **Ordovician** and **Silurian** the outlines of geosynclines and cratons remained unchanged. After various preliminary phases the Caledonian mountain-building, which culminated in the transition Silurian-Devonian, first wrought a fundamental paleogeographic transformation. The Caledonian geosyncline in northwest Europe was folded, and the old connection between the Baltic-Russian Shield and the Hebrides-Greenland mass was thereby restored. A less extensive fold-chain existed on the southwest border of Fennosarmatia. The northern block, thus formed, constituted the framework for the areas of subsidence of central and southern Europe which now entered the Variscan geosynclinal epoch. At the same time it became a landmass, the Old Red continent. The elevation of the Caledonian mountains was particularly vigorous and the adjoining parts of Fennosarmatia were also raised in the process. In this manner Fennoscandia originated; it has remained an epeirogenically positive area until today. The eastern half of Fennosarmatia, the Russian platform, which had been an uplift area in the earlier Paleozoic, now reversed its behavior and subsided. From the **Devonian** onward it was covered with continental and epicontinental-marine sediments. A paleogeographic map of the Devonian therefore resembles that of the latest Algonkian. The "Old Red" corresponds in facies and distribution with the "Oldest Red" of the Jotnian.

At the beginning of the **Carboniferous** tectonic unrest in the Variscan geosyncline increased. The inner chains of the Variscan mountains were folded, rose above sealevel, and sent their clastic erosion products into the surrounding shallow sea. The Kulm facies of the Lower Carboniferous embraced, as an aureole, the growing mountains, whereas in the more distant periphery, in northwest Europe, North Africa, and Russia, deposition of richly fossiliferous, commonly reef-, limestone proceeded from the Devonian into the Carboniferous. The second orogenic culmination followed during the transition to the Upper Carboniferous; it completed the Variscan mountains and pushed the sea back into the fore-deeps. The one, in front of the northern mainland, was well pronounced; the other, in front of the African primeval craton was less developed. During the Upper Carboniferous the marginal troughs shifted further outwards as the sea receded. The northern foredeep in central and northern Europe thereby considerably overlapped the northern mainland. At the same time it shoaled and thereby created the requisite conditions for the distribution of paralic coal-forming swamps. Coal-formation also occured in the inner depressions within the Variscan chain, likewise promoted by the humid climate. In comparison with the extended ranges of the Caledonian mountains separated by large overthrusts from their foreland, the Variscan mountains occupy a more compact area. In fact, it consists of several orogenes, each of which grew in length and breadth from a central zone by incorporating younger chains. The latest folds arose from the foredeeps which followed the outer margins of the Variscides.

In the Lower **Permian** the geocraty reaches a climax; the more so as at the time the Ural geosyncline as the last of the Variscan regions of subsidence was folded and became dry. But at the same time in other regions new transgressions were set in motion. The land connection Europe-Greenland, which was produced in the Caledonian orogeny, was cut off again in the Stephanian by a projecting bay of the sea, which extended from the Arctic via Spitzbergen as far as the North Sea.

From here Europe was flooded by the sea which deposited the Zechstein. More important were the epeirogenic inversions in the Mediterranean region, where the first establishment of the Alpine geosyncline took place. Here, also, the Variscan folding had created extensive land surfaces, which were, however, to sink under water shortly afterwards as a result of a transgression that advanced from Asia toward the W. In the southern Alps the geosyncline ended in the highest Upper Carboniferous; westward from Sicily, in the Permian.

In the highest **Triassic** even the western Mediterranean had been filled with marine waters. The Alpine geosyncline thereby reached its full extent and linked up with the world-encircling Tethys. The inherited tendency of southern Europe to subside manifested itself anew and became all the more conspicuous paleogeographically because the sea remained almost entirely restricted to the geosynclinal areas in Europe during the Permian and Triassic. Only temporary epicontinental transgressions overlapped the borders.

In the **Jurassic** the situation was entirely different. Shallow seas flooded not only central and western Europe which had been consolidated by the Variscan and Caledonian orogenies, but also the Russian platform. Only a few higher areas remained standing above sealevel — in the N Fenno-scandia and the Urals, and a chain of islands along the northern edge of Tethys, including the Spanish Meseta, the Central Massif of France, and the Rhenish-Ardennes, Bohemian, and Ukrainian Massifs.

The Alpine orogeny commenced in the Middle **Cretaceous** with folding of the central zones of the young mountain chains. A series of tectonic processes that were similar to those at the end of the Paleozoic followed. The main geosynclines became smaller because of rising fold-ranges. These migrated outward toward the borderlands and were finally reduced into two foredeeps. At the same time a regional uplift began which transformed the foredeeps into freshwater basins or dry land, and pushed back the open sea from the perimeter of the mountains. The first steps of this process, which fell within the Cretaceous, were limited wholly to the Tethys geosyncline. The pre-Gosauan orogeny in the central Alps, Carpathians, and Dinarides, created the main lines of the present-day Decken structure. Consequently, the flysch facies began to spread over numerous troughs. Meanwhile, the regions outside the Alps were scarcely influenced by this Alpine folding. Late Mesozoic crustal movements also took place in central and northwestern Europe, but they were restricted to Saxonic fault-folds and fell temporarily in other orogenic phases. The epicontinental flooding of the foreland attained its greatest extent in the Upper Cretaceous; at the transition to the Tertiary a sharp regression followed.

In the **Tertiary** the effects of the Alpine mountain-building extended much farther into the foreland. Two chief orogenic phases may be distinguished; the thrusting of the flysch foredeeps at the end of the Eocene or in the Oligocene; and the folding of the molasse basins at the middle or end of the Miocene. The London and Paris basins became dry as a consequence of these phases, and the North Sea, Black Sea, and Caspian were reduced to their present boundaries. From the late Tertiary onwards the regressions were followed by transgressions that proceeded from the subsidence and fragmentation of the Alpine chain. In the modern Mediterranean area and in southeast Europe, a series of older massifs — the Pannonian mass, the Tyrrhenian and Valachian-Euxine ridge — sank. The Alps were separated from the Carpathians by the Vienna basin, from the Pyrenees by the Rhône graben.

In the **Quaternary** the geocraty attained a climax in which glaciation and regression augmented each other. Glaciation was intensified by widespread uplifts; regression of the strandline was sharpened by eustatic lowering of sealevel.

Europe has been built step-by-step by adding younger mountain chains to the periphery of an old nucleus. The growth of the continent took place principally from the N toward the S. Fennosarmatia was considerably enlarged by the addition respectively of the Caledonian and Variscan fold tracts in Norway and central Europe. The African primeval craton grew much less. In this way the geosynclinal areas were always forced further S. This tendency has continued until recently. The only remains of Tethys that were not caught up in the Alpine orogeny are found south of the Alpine mountain chain. Each of the major mountain-building episodes, however, always added only a part of the folded areas to the then existing

cratons. The remainder either rigidified into small single massifs of subsided again to be refolded in later phases. Thus, in the substructure of the
Alps, we encounter Variscan, Caledonian, perhaps even older unconformities. But, though the later geosynclines each time took back with them
parts of older orogenes, the area still susceptible to folding shrank increasingly in the course of time. The nappe structure and the arcuate
bending of the Alpine chain may be attributed to its compression in a
progressively narrowing space.

In conclusion one may ask if the latest orogenes have exhausted the
possibilities for mountain-building in Europe. This is improbable. In the
Mediterranean a part of the Alpine chain is reverting to the geosynclinal
stage. A similar process is beginning in the North Atlantic where practically
the entire Hebridean Massif and a considerable part of the Caledonian
chain have almost completely sunk again.

Index of geographic and paleogeographic terms

T = Table opp. p. . . .